SILVER EDUCATIONAL PUBLISHING
SEPBOOKS.COM

KEY FACTS FOR ANATOMY AND PHYSIOLOGY

Dr. Patrick Leonardi

Silver Educational Publishing
Published by Silver 8 Production LLC

Copyright 2003, 2005 by Silver 8 Production LLC. All Rights Reserved.

ISBN 0-9719996-9-4

Disclaimer of Warranty and Limit of Liability:
The publisher and author have utilized great diligence and care in creating this book. However, the publisher and author make no representations or warranties with regards to the completeness or accuracy of the contents of this book and specifically disclaim all warranties, express or implied, including implied warranties of merchantability or fitness for a particular purpose. No warranty may be made or extended by written sales material or by salespersons or representatives of this company. The opinions of the author and the correctness and completeness of the information presented in this book are not warranted or guaranteed to produce any particular, general and/or specific results. Any information, suggestions, recommendations, advice, information and strategies contained in this book may not be appropriate for every person. Neither the author nor publisher shall be liable for any loss of profit or any other non-commercial or commercial damages, including but not limited to consequential, incidental, special, or other damages. Neither the publisher nor author assumes any liability for any damage and/or injury to persons or property arising from this book.

Any trademarks of which the publisher or author has knowledge of are in Initial Capital Letters and are owned by the appropriate companies or individuals. Owners of these trademarks are in no way affiliated with the publisher or author of this book.

Silver 8 Production LLC and Silver Educational Publishing are trademarks of Silver 8 Production LLC.

Contents

<u>**Notice to the Students**</u>

If you find this book helpful, please feel free to recommend this book in a review or simply just tell your classmates about it. Spreading the word about this book can help other students as well.

I. Medical Terminology: Word Structure and Origins

In most cases, it is much easier to remember the word root of a word in order to figure out its meaning. Here is a list of common word roots, prefixes (beginning of words) and suffixes (endings of words) used in many common medical words. If you know these word roots, prefixes and suffixes, you will find it easier to understand the medical language of doctors and other health care providers. Primary care providers consist of medical doctors, podiatrists, dentists, chiropractors, and optometrists (eye doctors). Health care providers can be doctors but also nurses, physical therapists, and physician assistants to name a few. Study these terms carefully. Anatomy refers to the structure of the body and physiology pertains to the function the body.

acou- sound or hearing
acro- extremity (Example: acromegaly is an enlargement of the toes, face and hands.)
adeno- related to a gland in the body.
algia- pain (Example: cephalgia is defined as a pain in the head, which is also known as a headache.)
andro- man
angi- a blood vessel (Example: angiocardigraphy is an x-ray of the structures and vessels around the heart.)
ante- before
anterior- front (Example: The face is anterior to the back of the head.)
arthro- joint
athero- fatty (Example: atherosclerosis)
auto- pertaining to self

bio- life (Example: biology is the study of life.)
blephar- eyelid
brachi- arm (Example: the biceps brachii is a muscle in the upper arm.)
bronch- relating to area near the lungs, branches of the windpipe
bucc- cheek (Example: The buccinator is a muscle found in the cheek area of the face.)

capit- head
carcin- malignant or cancerous (Example: Cigarettes contain many harmful

carcinogens.)

cardia- heart

cephal- towards the head or pertaining to the head. (Example: the neck is cephalic to the feet).

cerebro- brain

cervic- neck (Example: there are 7 cervical vertebrae in the neck.)

cheil- lips

chole-gallbladder (Example: cholecystitis is an inflammation of the gallbladder).

colp- vagina

contra- against, not recommended (Example: penicillin is contraindicated for a patient who is allergic to such a drug.)

crani-skull

cryo- cold (Example: physical therapists use ice packs, which is a form of cryotherapy on patients with ankle injuries.)

cyan- blue

cyt- cell (Example: cytology is the study of cells.)

dactyl- pertaining to fingers or toes

dent- tooth

derm- skin (Example: dermatologist is a skin doctor.)

dys- difficulty

ectomy- removing by surgery or cutting (Example: thyroidectomy is the surgical removal of the thyroid, which is a gland located in the neck.)

emia- blood

endo- inside (Example: endometrium is the lining inside the uterus.)

epi- around

erythro- red (Example: The erythrocyte refers to a red blood cell.)

gastro- stomach

gingiv- gums (Example: gingivitis is an inflammation of the gums.)

graph- record

gyn- woman (Example: gynecology is the study of diseases of the female reproductive system.)

hemi- half

hemo- blood (Example: hemoglobin is a substance in red blood cells that

brings oxygen to parts of the body)

hepato- liver

hist- tissue (Example: histology is the study of tissues.)

hydro- water

hyper- high amount (Example: muscle hypertrophy is a elevated growth of muscle tissue.)

hypo- low, below surface of skin

hystero- uterus (Example: hysterectomy is the surgical removal of the uterus).

iatro- doctor

infra- beneath (Example: the infrapatellar fat pad is located under the patella, which is the knee bone.)

inter- between

intra- inside (Example: the intraocular pressure occurs inside the eye.)

iso- same

itis- inflammation (Example: tendonitis is inflammation of the tendons.)

lacto- milk

latero- side (Example: the shoulder is lateral to the neck.)

lithos- stone

lingu- tongue (Example: the lingual tonsils are located near the bottom of the tongue.

lipo- fat

logy- the study of (Example: histology is the study of tissues.)

lysis- splitting, breaking apart

macro- large (Example: macrophages are large white blood cells that eat bacteria.)

mal- bad, abnormal

mammo- breast (Example: mammary glands are located in the breasts.)

mast- breast

mega- large

melan- black (Example: melanoma is the natural occurring pigment in skin that is responsible for the different shades of skin color.)

meta- after

micro- small (Example: microglia are cells found in the nervous system that destroy bacteria.)

myo- muscle

myc- fungus (Example: mycology is the study of fungi.)

myelo- marrow

neo- new

necro- death (Example: necrosis is a form of tissue death.)

noct- night

nephro- kidney (Example: the nephron is the functional unit of the kidney.)

neuro- nerve

null- none

oculo- eye (Example: the oculomotor nerve is the cranial nerve of the eye.)

oligo- small amount

oma- tumor (Example: lipoma is a tumor of fat found most commonly under the skin.)

onco- tumor (Example: an oncologist is a medical doctor that specializes in tumor diagnosis).

ortho- straight

osteo- bone (Example: osteology is the study of bones.)

osis- condition of

ot- ear (Example: otorhinolaryngology is the a medical specialty that deals with the diagnosis of diseases of the ears, nose and throat.)

pan- all

path- disease (Example: pathology is the study of disease.)

ped- child

penia- deficiency (Example: leukopenia is a deficiency of leukocytes or white blood cells in the blood.)

peri- around

phago- eat (Example: macrophage are large white blood cells that eat bacteria in the body.)

poly- many

pharyng- throat (Example: the nasopharynx is the upper portion of the throat.)

phleb- vein

phobia- fear (Example: phobias cause unrealistic anxiety in people.)

plasty- repair

plegia- paralysis (Example: quadriplegia mean there is paralysis of both

arms and legs.)

pnea- breathing

post- after (Example: postmaturity refers to a pregnancy lasting more than 42 weeks in length.)

posterior- back

pseudo- false (Example: a pseudotumor in the brain gives the same symptoms of a brain tumor. However, it is not a brain tumor.)

pulmo- lung

rhag- burst (Example: hemorrhage results in blood loss from the body.)

rrhea- flow, discharge

rhino- nose (Example: allergic rhinitis is an allergy that causes itching of the nose and eyes with sneezing.)

sclero- hard

scope- instrument (Example: a stethoscope is an in instrument a doctor uses to listen for abnormal heart sounds, and abnormal blood flow in vessels in the chest and abdomen.)

scopy- examination

semi- half

stasis- maintaining a certain level consistently (Example: stasis dermatitis is a chronic (occurring frequently) condition where there is red, scaly skin of the lower legs.)

stom- mouth

super- superficial, on the surface (Example: the skin is considered superficial.)

supra- above

tachy- fast (Example: tachycardia is an abnormally fast heartbeat.)

therap- treatment

thermo- heat (Example: thermography is a test that looks for changes in body temperature.)

thorac- chest

thrombo- clot (Example: thrombocytes are cells in the blood that make blood clot. Without thrombocytes a person would keep bleeding from a small cut.)

trans- across, through

toxi- poison (Example: toxicology is the study and treatment of poisons.)

uria- urine

vaso- vessel (Example: vasodilation is increase in the inside of a blood vessel. In this way, more blood enters the blood vessel.)

veno- vein

xero- dry (Example: xerophthalmia is a condition where part of the eye called the cornea gets dry.)

II. The Cell

Structure (Organelles), Function and Specialization

Cells are the basic units of animals, plants and bacteria. Each cell has organelles, which are the structures with specific shapes that carry out functions. The main parts of a cell are the cytoplasm, cell membrane and nucleus. Cells can carry out functions such as reproduction, digestion and movement.

Nucleus is circular in shape and is the center of the cell. Since it contains genes (DNA), it is important for reproduction of the cell. It is the largest organelle.

Cell membrane is the outer portion of the cell. It transports material from the outside to inside the cell. It is composed of fats and proteins.

Cytoplasm is all the contents of the cell between the cell membrane and the nucleus.

Endoplasmic reticulum is made of canals and sac-like structures. It is important for the making of protein in the cell.

Microtubules aid in the movement of substances in the cytoplasm.

Lysosomes function in digestion of proteins and other substances.

Mitochondria produce ATP, which is a substance needed for muscles to work and perform properly. Mitochondria are the powerhouses of the cell. Without these organelles, there is little energy for the cell to work.

Ribosomes also make proteins.

Nucleolus located in the nucleus. It is responsible for the creation of ribosomes.

Golgi Complex consists of four to eight sacs. Its primary function is to deliver proteins and fats to the lysosome.

The Cell's Relationship to Tissues
(Epithelial, Connective, Muscular, & Nervous), Organs and Systems

Tissues are collections of similar cells that work together to carry out specific functions. Tissues are found around all organs of the body. The human body develops from one cell. During the second week of growth of the human fetus, three specific layers of cells form, which consist of the following:

1. **Endoderm** is the inner layer of the fetus and forms the lining of the digestive and respiratory tracts.

2. **Mesoderm** is the middle layer of the fetus and forms muscles, bones, blood, connective tissues and linings of most organs.

3. **Ectoderm** is the outer layer of the fetus and forms the outer layer of skin called the epidermis.

There are four types of tissue in the body and include the following: epithelial (skin), connective, muscular and nervous tissue.

* **Epithelial tissue** covers the surface of the body in the form of skin. It is also located around *organs, body cavities and produces glands*. Epithelial tissue has functions of protection, excretion, and absorption to name a few. Epithelial cells comes in different shapes. Squamous cells are flat, cuboidal cells are shaped like ice cubes, and columnar cells are tall and rectangular. However, there are transitional cells that change shape. For example, transitional cells are around the urinary bladder. Transitional cells expand when urine fills the bladder. In this way, the bladder can withstand great amounts of liquid without breaking open. Transitional cells range in shape from columnar to cuboidal.

When observing the thickness of epithelium, there are 3 types which consists of the following:

1. Stratified Epithelium is two or more layers thick. This is the "wear and tear" type of epithelium. So organs that are used a lot get this type of epithelium around them. For example. the esophagus is part of the throat where food goes down into the stomach. As you can imagine, food goes down this organ for at least 3 meals a day. This causes a lot of wear and tear.

2. Simple Epithelium is one layer thick. There is less wear and tear here so one layer of skin cells is sufficient. For example, the ear drum's inner

surface has simple epithelium.

3. *Pseudostratified epithelium* appears as stratified epithelium but has only one layer of skin cells. In other words, pseudostratified is most similar to stratified epithelium.

* **Connective tissue** supports the body, prevents friction between bone joints and fastens structures together. There is a gel-like structure in connective tissue that is between cells and structures of the body. Connective tissue also contains collagen, which is a very strong protein that is very flexible and quite resistant to breaking. Collagen is the most plentiful protein in the body. There are several types of connective tissue, which consists of the following:

1. *Loose connective tissue* connects the skin to the underlying tissues. Loose connective tissue also fills up the spaces between muscles in the body. There are three types of loose connective tissue:

    a. Areolar connective tissue is the most common type.

    b. Adipose tissue is tissue made of fat cells that are used as a form of heat and fat storage. Fat cells are called adipocytes. Adipose tissue also protects organs from injury. Adipose tissue is found in the stomach area, heart, around the kidneys, between muscles and under the skin.

    c. Reticular connective tissue is located in the liver and it also helps to bind cells of involuntary muscle called smooth muscle. This type of muscle is not controlled under voluntary action.

2. *Dense connective tissue* consists of three types: dense regular connective tissue, dense irregular connective tissue, elastic connective tissue.

3. *Cartilage* consists of three types:

    a. Hyaline cartilage is blue and white in color; it is the most abundant type of cartilage in the body. It gives flexibility and reduces shock absorption and friction around joints. A great portion of the nose is composed of hyaline cartilage.

    b. Elastic cartilage gives strength and flexibility and preserves shape of some organs.

    c. Fibrocartilage is found between vertebrae, which are the bones of the spine. Fibrocartilage is in the form of discs. For example, when

you hear of someone having a herniated disc, the fibrocartilage is damaged leading to reduced flexibility and pain in some cases.

4. *Bone Tissue* is classified as either a dense (compact) or spongy (cancellous) type of connective tissue. Bone tissue consists mostly of calcium phosphate (mineral salt) and some calcium carbonate and collagen. The collagen is needed in bone to keep the bone from being too brittle and breaking too easily. Calcium phosphate is responsible for the hardness of bone.

 * **Muscular Tissue** has a primary function, which is the movement of body parts. It does this by the action of muscle contraction. There are three types of muscle tissue which are the following:

1. *Skeletal muscle* is attached to bone or other muscles and are controlled voluntarily. In this way, it is called voluntary muscle. They are also striated because under a microscope that have light and dark markings.

2. *Smooth muscle* is located in the walls of organs; it is not under conscious control. In fact, it is called an involuntary muscle. Smooth muscle can be located in the stomach, intestines, urinary bladder, blood vessels and gallbladder. Smooth muscle is non-striated.

3. *Cardiac muscle* is found exclusively in the heart. It is also striated and controlled involuntary. Thus, it is an involuntary muscle. The heart will still continue to beat even without being directly stimulated by nerve impulses. This is because there is an intrinsic mechanism of the heart to keep beating.

 * **Nervous Tissue** consists of neurons, which are nerve cells. Neurons are the structural and functional units of the nervous system, and they conduct nerve impulses so muscles can contract and cause a body movement. Think of nerve impulses as messages that nerves give to muscles to contract or relax. Connective and supportive tissue in the nervous system are referred to as neuroglia.

 * **Organs and Systems** are made from cells. The organism (the human being) is the sum total of the chemicals, cells, tissues, organs and systems of the body. Let's start with the smallest part of the body, which is chemicals.

Chemicals are made of molecules. Example of chemicals include the following: hormones, proteins, enzymes, vitamins and lipids (fats). Cells are the basic units of an organism. Each cell has organelles, which are the structures that carry out functions. For example, the mitochondria in a cell carry out cellular respiration. Tissues are made up of cells. The tissues of the body consist of nervous tissue, muscle tissue, epithelial tissue and connective tissue. The organ performs a specific function. For example, the heart pumps blood through out the body. The system is made of organs that perform functions and work as a team for a larger result. For example, the digestive system consists of the mouth, pharynx, esophagus, stomach, small intestine, teeth, tongue, salivary glands, pancreas and gallbladder. Each organ performs a specific function so the digestive system can perform the ultimate goal of digestion most efficiently. The organism consists of all the parts of the body working together. The correct order from smallest to largest can be observed:

Chemicals--Cells--Tissues--Organs--Systems--Organism

Cell Metabolism

Cell Metabolism consists of the all the chemical reactions in a cell that contribute to its growth and maintenance, including anabolism & catabolism. **Anabolism** is the building up of small parts of the body into larger ones. For example, a two-year-old infant will grow approximately to twice his or her height at full physical maturity. In this way, this is a form of anabolism on a larger scale.
Catabolism is the breaking down of large molecules into smaller ones. Digestion, which is the breaking down of large pieces of food into smaller ones, is an example.

Diseases, Medical Terminology and Clinical Procedures

Oncology is the study of tumors. An oncologist is a medical doctor that specializes in diagnosing and treating tumors.
Neoplasm is also known as a tumor or growth. Neoplasm can be spotted on x-ray or MRI. Neoplasm (Tumor) can either be diagnosed as:
Malignant = cancerous   or   *Benign = not cancerous*

Metastasis (*pronounce it like me-TAS-ta-sis*) is a fancy word meaning

cancer spreading. For example, if a cancerous tumor is found in the breast and remains there, it is referred to as a localized cancer. However, if this cancerous tumor spreads to the brain, it is referred to as metastasis. The cancer spread from the breast to the brain. However, cancer can spread to any part of the body; it is not only limited to the brain.

Biopsy is the removal of a tissue of the body for microscopic observation in order to make a diagnosis. It is used most commonly as a test for cancer.

Dysplasia is the abnormal growth in the size and shape of cells.

Metaplasia is the change from one type of cell into another.

Progeny- offspring

Adhesion is the abnormal union of tissues.

Laceration is the tearing of the skin, producing deep cuts sometimes with gross deformity.

Nevus is referred to as mole or beauty mark.

Pruritis is an intense itching, which can be caused by a skin infection.

Topical refers to the surface or superficial part of the something. A topical cream is to be applied on the skin and not swallowed or injected.

Dermatology is the study of skin conditions and diseases.

Basal Cell Carcinoma is the most common type of skin cancer. Lesions can appear in an array of colors. Most cancerous lesions are irregular in shape; they are not symmetrical. In other words, cancerous lesions are usually not circular in shape. Rarely, does this type of cancer spread (metastasize). Skin cancer can be prevented by using a sunscreen of 30 SPF or more all year round. Make sure areas of the ear, face and back of neck are protected with sunscreen, and of course, any exposed parts.

Malignant Melanoma is the most deadly form of skin cancer. This is because this type rapidly spreads from a cancer of the skin to other parts of the body. Remember that cancerous lesions are usually raised and irregular in shape. Non-cancerous lesions are usually flat.

Cerebral Contusion is a condition where the brain is bruised usually by a strong blow to the head.

Psoriasis is a skin condition where there is an dramatic increase in the growth of skin cells. This leads to scales or flakes on the skin that are white and silver in color. There is no known cure, yet, for this condition.

Macules are also known as freckles. They are less than 1 cm in diameter.

III. The Digestive System

Structure and Function
(Ingestion/Absorption, Digestion, Excretion, Nutrition)

Food must undergo many chemical and physical changes before it is digested and absorbed into the blood for nutrition. Here is a list of digestive processes:

Ingestion is the process of eating.

Digestion is the physical and mechanical processes used by the body to break down food.

Absorption is the passage of digested food to the cells of the body.

Defecation is the elimination of food that is not digested in the form of feces.

Enzymes are small protein molecules in the body that break down large food pieces into smaller ones. In this way, they make digestion a lot easier and efficient.

There are two types of organs for digestion which are the following:
-*gastrointestinal tract (GI tract)*
-*accessory structures*
The gastrointestinal tract is a tube that starts from the mouth and ends at the anus. Digestion actually starts in the mouth. The organs of the gastrointestinal tract consist of the following:

1. mouth
2. pharynx
3. esophagus
4. stomach
5. small intestine
6. large intestine

The accessory structures are the second group of organs that make up the digestive system, which are the following:

1. teeth
2. tongue
3. salivary glands
4. liver
5. gallbladder
6. pancreas

Digestion by the Organs of the Gastrointestinal Tract

When food is chewed by the teeth, it is called *mastication*. The saliva in the mouth contains digestive enzymes or chemicals that break down food at a faster rate. For example, the enzymes can digest starches and turn them into sugar. When the food is finally swallowed, the medical term for swallowing is called *deglutition*. The ball of food called the bolus goes down the pharynx located in the throat. The food now travels from the pharynx to the esophagus, which starts at the throat and ends at the stomach. Remember the food moves down the esophagus from smooth muscle contraction. Smooth muscle automatically moves the food without having to think about it. Smooth muscle is an involuntary muscle. From the esophagus the food goes to the stomach where it is broken down into small pieces by the high concentrations of acids in the stomach. These small pieces of food now enter the small intestine. The small intestine consists of three parts: *duodenum, jejunum, and ileum.* The small pieces of food now first enter the duodenum, then the jejunum and finally the ileum. The small intestine continues to break down the food even more with digestive enzymes. It is interesting to note that the longest part of the gastrointestinal tract is the small intestine. It is approximately 20 feet long. Most food particles are absorbed in the small intestine. In this way, all cells of the body can get the proper nutrition if our diet is healthy. Vitamins A, D, E and K are absorbed in the small intestine. We are what we eat. If one eats lots of fatty foods with animal proteins, the cells of the body will not work as efficiently and eventually can lead to a risk of malfunction or disease. However, eating a diet consisting of whole grains, plant proteins, fruits and vegetables will not only maintain a healthy system but contribute to a healthy mind. Plant proteins can come in the form of soy milk, beans, whole wheat bread. It is a myth that eating animal proteins is the only way to get big muscles or to gain muscle. Gorillas are vegetarians (they get their protein from plant sources to build muscles) and some do have the strength of 10 men. Of course, one needs also to exercise one's muscles to gain muscle.

Now after food is digested and absorbed in the small intestine, there is still some undigested food left. This undigested food enters the large intestine from the ileum of the small intestine. The first part of the large intestine that this undigested food enters is called the cecum. After the cecum it enters the ascending colon, transverse colon, descending colon, and sigmoid colon, which is S-shaped. From the sigmoid colon, the feces is stored in the

rectum. When one goes to the bathroom or defecates, the feces moves from the rectum to the anal canal and finally out through the anus. The total length of the large intestine is 5 feet. The last stage of digestion actually occurs in the colon. This is because any undigested food that is not completely broken down, is done so by the bacteria that live there.

Accessory Structures of the Digestive System

Liver is located in the upper abdominal area. The liver makes bile, which is a substance needed for the breaking down and absorption of fats by the body.

Gallbladder is located in the left abdominal area. It is a place where bile is stored. When fats that enter the small intestine need to be broken down, the gall bladder sends bile to the small intestine. In this way, fats can be digested and absorbed by the body.

Pancreas is located in the upper, central abdominal area. It is a about 5 inches long. It has ducts or tubes connected to the jejunum of the small intestine. The pancreas secretes or gives pancreatic juice to the small intestine. The pancreatic juice contains enzymes that help the small intestines digest different foods. Pancreatic juice has enzymes that can help the small intestine break down the following: proteins, starches, and fats.

Tongue is used to mix the food in the mouth with saliva. It helps in swallowing and in lining up food to chew.

Salivary Glands secrete saliva. Saliva makes food wet so its easier to digest. The chemical digestion of carbohydrates like bread and pasta (starch) begins here. The three salivary glands consists of the following:
-*Parotid gland (located in front of ear)*
-*Submandibular gland (located in the lower jaw area)*
-*Sublingual (located under the tongue)*

Teeth are used to break down food into smaller pieces. Teeth chew on food, which is a process call mastication. Saliva consists of the enzyme amylase that breaks down carbohydrates into simple sugars. Saliva is actually 99.5 % water.

Nutrition

Vitamin A is important for normal vision, defense against bacteria and healthy skin. It is an antioxidant. Antioxidants fight against free-radicals,

which cause cancer. A deficiency will cause night blindness. So be careful when you drive at night if you don't have enough Vitamin A. Excessive amounts will cause temporary baldness in some areas of the scalp and joint pain. Sources of Vitamin A include: fish liver oils, egg yolks, and butter.

Vitamin D is formed in the skin with sun exposure and in certain foods we eat. This vitamin is needed for proper absorption of calcium by the small intestine so bones can be strong. 10 minutes of sun exposure is what is needed for your body to make Vitamin D. Food sources of Vitamin D include: soy milk, egg yolks, fish liver oil. A deficiency will cause softening of bones, muscle spasm and abnormal bone growth. Excessive amounts will cause vomiting, frequent urination, itching, nausea and nervousness.

Vitamin K is important for blood to clot. For example, if you cut yourself and your body has no Vitamin K, the cut will keep bleeding. Vitamin K actually helps the blood to clot or stop bleeding. Food sources include: green leafy vegetables and vegetable oil.

Vitamin B$_1$ or thiamine helps the heart and nerves to function properly. Food sources include: yeast, whole wheat bread, beans and potatoes. Deficiency can cause abnormal nerve and heart function.

Vitamin E is an antioxidant. Food sources consist of: green leafy vegetables, eggs, beans and wheat. Deficiency will cause red blood cell damage and destruction to the nerves.

Vitamin B$_2$ or riboflavin is needed for proper metabolism of carbohydrates. Food sources include: eggs, soy milk, and dairy products. Deficiency will cause flaky, red skin (dermatitis).

Vitamin B$_3$ or niacin is also need for proper metabolism of carbohydrates. Food sources include the following: yeast, beans, fish, and whole grains. Deficiency will cause skin disorders and inflammation of the tongue.

Vitamins B$_5$ or pyridoxine is needed for the metabolism of fat and carbohydrates. Food sources include the following: green leafy vegetables. Deficiency will cause nerve problems.

Vitamin B$_6$ or pyridoxine is needed for healthy skin and proper nerve function. Food sources include the following: fish, yeast, and beans. Deficiency will cause skin disorders and anemia, which is a low amount of red blood cells or hemoglobulin (Refer to P.20) in the blood. Anemia will make one tired because there is less oxygen in the blood. This is because red blood cells carry oxygen to the heart and lungs.

Vitamin B$_9$ or folic acid is needed for proper red blood cell function.

Vitamin B₁₂ or cobalamin is needed for proper red blood cell and nerve function. Food sources include the following: eggs, soy milk, diary products. Deficiency can cause anemia and poor vision.

Vitamin C is needed for proper bone and connective tissue growth. Also Vitamin C is an antioxidant. It serves great to protect the skin from sun damage. However, sunscreen is always required when going outside. Food sources: tomato sauce, tomatoes, peppers, cabbage and various fruits such as oranges and strawberries.

Diseases, Medical Terminology and Clinical Procedures

Mumps is an inflammation of the parotid gland, which is a salivary gland. It is caused by the myxovirus also known as the mumps virus. Symptoms include the following: fever, weakness, pain in the throat and pain when swallowing. Swelling occurs on both sides of face.

Hemorrhoids are also known as piles. Hemorrhoids are veins in the rectum that are bigger than normal and are inflamed. Symptoms include itching and bleeding. Diet low in fiber can cause hemorrhoids and constant straining when going to the bathroom is another factor.

Dental Caries is also known as tooth decay. Flossing after each and every meal will prevent cavities and gingivitis, which is an inflammation of the gums with bleeding and some gum recession. Gum recession makes the teeth look longer.

Gastrectomy is surgical removal of the stomach.

Dysphagia is a difficulty in swallowing.

Enteritis is an inflammation of the small intestine.

Flatulence is excessive gas.

Hepatitis is an inflammation of the liver. It comes usually in four types which are the following:

1. Hepatitis A is a virus that is transmitted through food. Especially, when one of the workers from the restaurant has not cleaned their hands after going to bathroom. In other words, this is transmitted through the fecal-oral route. Symptoms of hepatitis are anorexia, yellowing of the skin, tender liver, nausea, weakness and enlargement of the liver.

2. Hepatitis B is a virus transmitted through needle sharing and unprotected sex. However, this type has a long incubation period from one to six months. A long incubation period means it takes between one to six months

for the disease to show symptoms. Type B tends to be more severe than Type A and Type C.

3. Hepatitis C is a virus transmitted primarily through blood transfusions. It still can be transmitted through unprotected sex and sharing of needles. This type tends to last for years.

4. Hepatitis D usually occurs as a co-infection with Hepatitis B. Thus, this makes the symptoms worse of Hepatitis B.

Hepatomegaly is an enlargement of the liver.

Cholecystitis is an inflammation of the gallbladder than can be caused by gallstones or bacterial infection. There are floating stools or feces that are pencil thin, pain is sudden and quite severe and vomiting is present. Generally, women over 40 who are fertile and overweight are prime candidates.

Gallstones are formed from the union of cholesterol and bile.

Cholelithiasis (pronounced ko-le-li-THI-a-sis) is simply the occurrence of gallstones.

Diverticulitis is a disease of the large intestine. In this condition, the wall of the large intestines build up pouches or little indentations where food particles get stuck and cause inflammation. The stuck food particles ferment and cause added bacteria in the large intestine that should not be there. High meat diet is a definitely a cause of this condition. This is because meat takes a lot longer to be digested. Since meat is low in fiber, the full content of meat does not make it to the rectum to be defecated as feces. Extra fiber in the diet can be attained by eating fruits and vegetables.

Endoscopy is a tube with lenses that is put into the body to visualize certain structures in the body. It is used to examine for tumors, inflammation, or internal bleeding.

Percussion is an examination technique used by placing one finger over a body part and tapping it with another finger. You tap your middle finger with your pointer finger over a patient's body part. For instance, the heart, abdomen and lungs can be assessed for any tumors or masses that should not be there. The tapping is used to assess the sound. Certain sounds like flat or dull mean different things. Generally, percussion is used to find the location of organs and to assess whether they are too large.

Barium X-Ray Study is an x-ray study performed by getting the patient to

drink a dye. Soon after, the patient is x-rayed. This study is used to check for ulcers and tumors in the GI tract.

IV. Respiratory System

Structure and Function

The respiratory system consists of the following:
1. *nose*
2. *pharynx (throat)*
3. *larynx (voice box)*
4. *trachea (windpipe)*
5. *bronchi*
6. *lungs*

1. Nose acts as a filter of air. So it prevents large pollutants from entering the lungs. It also functions in the sense of smell. The nose is useful for heating air as you inhale and contributes to the sound of your voice.

2. Pharynx is a tube lined with smooth muscle. Basically, it is used for breathing and for passage of food into the esophagus and then finally to the stomach. There are 3 different parts of the pharynx, which consist of the following:

* The nasopharnyx helps in respiration.

* The oropharynx helps in respiration and digestion.

* The laryngopharynx also helps in respiration and digestion.

3. Larynx contains the voice box, which consists of vocal folds made of cartilage that vibrate and create sound. It also contains the Adam's Apple, which is made of thyroid cartilage. This organ links the pharynx with the trachea.

4. Trachea is also known as the windpipe. It starts at the end of the larynx and divides into two bronchi. The trachea is anterior to the epiglottis. Anterior means in front of or the front of something. For example, the chest is anterior to the back. To review, when one inhales, the air goes through the nose, to the pharynx, to the larynx, and then to the trachea.

5. Bronchi consist of the right primary bronchus and the left primary bronchus. Bronchi are tube-like. Both bronchi and trachea consist of rings of cartilage. It is also important to note that the right and left primary bronchi enter the lungs. Bronchi should be viewed as the stem of a tree.

This is because the right and left primary bronchus will divide and form smaller bronchi called secondary and tertiary bronchi, which are the branches of the tree. The tertiary bronchi will divide even further into bronchioles. From the trachea, air goes to the bronchi, where air will eventually enter the lungs.

6. *Lungs* consists of two organs. There is a right and left lung. The right lung has three lobes or parts. The left lung has two lobes or parts.

Respiration

Respiration is the exchange of gases in the atmosphere (oxygen) and the blood by inhaling and exhaling air. 12-18 breaths per minute is considered normal. Normal breathing is called eupnea (pronounced yoop-NE-a).

External Respiration is the exchange of gases between the lungs and the blood. Oxygen and carbon dioxide are the gases that are exchanged. It changes deoxygenated blood into oxygenated blood or blood that has oxygen.

Internal Respiration is the exchange of gases between the blood and tissue cells of the body. Oxygen and carbon dioxide are the gases that are exchanged. This results in the changing of oxygenated blood into deoxygenated blood.

Gas Exchange

The main purpose of respiration is to give the cells of the body a constant supply of oxygen. Oxygen is needed by the cells of the body to function. Without oxygen, organs will die. *Pulmonary ventilation or breathing* is the gas exchange between the air in the atmosphere and the cells in the lungs called alveoli. Alveoli are what gives the spongy structure to the lungs. Alveoli look like little grapes. They are actually called little air sacs. There are about 300 million alveoli in the lungs. Alveoli are responsible for bringing the oxygen from the atmosphere to enter the blood. As we inhale, oxygen comes in and when we exhale, carbon dioxide (waste product) comes out. Alveoli make this possible. This is because alveoli have direct connections with small blood vessels (capillaries) to let this happen. Oxygen is needed by every cell of the body to continue to exist. Without oxygen necrosis or cell death will occur soon after. For inspiration or inhalation to occur, lungs must get bigger or expand. In this way, the air

pressure inside the lungs is less than the air pressure in the atmosphere. Greater air pressure in the environment or atmosphere will push the air into the lungs. In order to exhale or breathe out, the lungs must decrease in size. In this way, the air pressure inside the lungs is now greater than the air pressure in the atmosphere. So greater air pressure will push the air out of the lungs and into the outside environment or atmosphere.

Hemoglobin is a substance in red blood cells that is very important for carrying oxygen from the air we breathe to the cells of our body. Hemoglobin consists of globin, which is a protein and hemo which is a pigment that contains iron. With decreased amounts of hemoglobin, anemia results leading to weakness and a lack of energy.

Lung Volumes

Tidal Volume is the total volume of air that enters all the respiratory organs with normal breathing. The total volume is approximately 500 ml.

Inspiratory Reserve Volume is simply the extra amount of air that can be inspired or inhaled beyond tidal volume. This would be an example of taking a deep breath in. Inspiratory reserve volume is 3100 ml. When taking a deep breathe, much more air can enter the lungs, and thus, more oxygen can get to all the tissues of the body from the blood.

Expiratory Reserve Volume the extra amount of air that can be exhaled or expired by forcing the air out of the lungs. This is equal to about 1200 ml.

Residual Volume is the amount of air that is still in the lungs even after you force all the air out. This is about 1200 ml. Since all organs need oxygen, there is always air left in the lungs even when you try to blow all the air out.

Diseases, Medical Terminology and Clinical Procedures

Laryngitis is an inflammation of the larynx. The most common cause is by a viral infection caused by the common cold. Symptoms and signs include the following: hoarseness of voice, loss of voice, throat feels raw and inflamed.

Symptoms are the what the patient actually experiences. Some examples include headache, heartburn, soar throat, and low back pain.

Signs are what the doctor observes in the patient. Some examples include, slurred speech, cross-eyes, bad posture, and flat feet.

Nebulization (pronounce neb-yoo-li-ZA-shun) is a procedure of medication by using air droplets. It usually comes in the form of a nebulizer that sprays a mist, which the person inhales. It can be used for respiratory conditions such as asthma.

Asthma is a respiratory condition where the breathing airways become narrowed by inflammation. In other words, the breathing airways are lined by smooth muscles, which go into spasm. This narrows the breathing airways. Causes of asthma include the following: dust mites, feathers, indoor pollutants, cigarette smoke and food preservatives such as sulfites found in vinegar.

Emphysema (pronounce em-fi-see-ma) is caused by destruction of the walls of the alveoli, which are the little air sacs of the lungs. Since the walls are destroyed, air gets trapped in the lungs. In this way, a patient with emphysema must consciously exhale especially during strenuous exercise. Emphysema is caused by years of inhaling cigarette smoke and other poisonous chemicals.

Tachypnea means rapid breathing.

Dyspnea is difficulty breathing.

Epistaxis is a nose bleed. It can be caused by tumors, allergies or blunt trauma.

Hemoptysis is spitting of blood.

Pneumonectomy is a surgical removal of the lung.

Rhinoplasty is a surgical procedure for fixing the cosmetic appearance of the nose. This is the medical term for a nose job.

Pneumonia is a lung affection where the alveoli fill up with fluid. Approximately, 60,000 people every year die of this condition in the United States. Symptoms include the following: chest pain, chills, and shortness of breath. Most causes of pneumonia are from bacteria. Most patients affected have low-immunity against disease, which include newborns, elderly, and A.I.D.S. patients.

Atelectasis is a collapse of a portion or of the entire lung. This can occur by a lung tumor or congestion of mucus in the lung.

CPR or cardiopulmonary resuscitation is a way of reestablishing respiration and blood circulation for a patient. Typically, this procedure is done for patients who have just experienced physical trauma as in drowning, choking, car accident, etc. The first procedure is to always check the person's *airway* to inspect for an obstruction, check for *breathing* and then the pulse for *circulation*. If the person is not breathing, mouth to mouth

resuscitation is given. If there is no pulse, chest compressions are given to get blood out of the heart and into circulation. Health care professionals must be CPR certified to perform this procedure.

Orthopnea is difficulty or shortness of breath while lying down.

Auscultation is performed by the doctor by using a stethoscope for listening to abnormal lung sounds. It can also be used for abnormal heart and stomach sounds. Certain sounds are associated with specific diseases. Experience and knowledge can make one quite skillful at auscultation.

Mammography is an x-ray test for breast cancer.

Aspiration is an inhalation of water, food or foreign matter into the lungs. This is not a good thing.

Scoliosis is the abnormal curvature of the spine. Some doctors treat it with bracing and chiropractic adjustments. Scoliosis can be prevented in some cases by making both sides of the body equally as strong. This can be done with a weight training and stretching program.

Asbestosis is fibrosis or scarring of lung tissue caused by breathing in asbestos dust. Asbestos inhalation can cause shortness of breath, inability to exercise and lung cancer.

Black Lung is a disease caused by inhalation of coal dust.

Psittacosis (pronounced sit-a-co-sis) or Parrot Fever is a type of pneumonia that is caused by certain bacteria found in birds. People who work at bird pet stores are most at risk. However, this condition is quite rare. More than 99% of bird owners never get this condition.

V. The Circulatory System

Structure and Function

The circulatory system consists of two parts, which are the blood-vascular system and the lymph-vascular system.

Blood-vascular system is made of the heart and blood vessels which consists of arteries, veins and capillaries. The purpose of this system is to circulate blood through out the body to all of its organs. In this way, all tissues and organs will get oxygen.

Lymph-vascular system is the lymphatic system, which will be discussed later. Briefly, lymph is a yellowish or clear substance that is important for immunity against bacteria and removal of waste products in the cells of the body. Lymph also provides nutrition from the blood to the cells of the

body. As you can see, the blood-vascular and lymph-vascular systems are related.

Heart and Blood Vessels

Heart is a cone-shaped organ that weighs about 10 ounces. It is about the size of a fist and pumps about 2000 gallons of blood per day. The heart is a muscular organ that contracts on its own without conscious thought. The heart is protected by a wall or membrane call the *pericardium*. The pericardium entirely surrounds the heart. The heart contains four chambers which are the following: left atrium, right atrium, left ventricle and right ventricle. The left atrium and the right atrium compose the upper portion of the heart. The left ventricle and the right ventricle compose the lower portion of the heart. The heart also has an *apex*, which is located at the bottom of the heart. The base of the heart is located at the top of the heart. The apex is the pointed end of the heart, which can be found approximately one inch below diagonally from the left nipple.

Epicardium is the outer layer of the heart.

Myocardium is the middle layer of the heart. Cardiac muscle fibers are present, which causes the heart to beat.

Endocardium is the inner layer of the heart.

Arteries bring blood from the heart to other tissues of the body. Arteries carry oxygenated blood from the heart and to the capillaries. Arteries, which are blood vessels have thick walls that are muscular and elastic. These vessels will look red since they have oxygenated blood in them.

Aorta is the largest artery of the body. It has a diameter of one inch. It is made of three parts which are the following:

1. Arch of Aorta is found on top of the heart.

2. Thoracic Aorta is found posterior to the heart or in the back of the heart. It is located in the middle of the back.

3. Abdominal Aorta is found near the belly button (umbilicus).

Capillaries are very small blood vessels. Usually, they can only be seen under a microscope. They actually link small arteries with veins. Capillaries have very thin walls. Capillaries help tissues and cells of the body receive nutrition (food). When the cells and tissues eat the food, there are waste products that result. These waste products are sent back to the capillaries. The capillaries will effectively eliminate these waste products by sending them to small veins.

Veins are thin-walled blood vessels that will get the waste products from the capillaries and send them to the heart. Veins are generally found closer to the skin. Arteries are deeper in the body.

Arterioles are small arteries.

Venules are referred to as small veins.

Arteries of the Head, Face and Neck

1. *Vertebral Artery*
2. *External Carotid Artery*
3. *Occipital Artery* is located near the back of the skull.
4. *Internal Carotid Artery*
5. *Posterior Auricular Artery* is located near the back of the ear.
6. *Superficial Temporal Artery* is located on the sides of the skull. It supplies blood to the forehead and the chewing muscle (will be discussed later) called the masseter.
7. *Parietal Artery* located posterior to the transverse artery.
8. *Frontal Artery* is located near the forehead.
9. *Supra-Orbital Artery* is located above the eye.
10. *Infra-Orbital Artery* is located below the eye.
11. *Transverse Facial Artery* is located in front of the ear, which means anterior to the ear. This artery supplies blood to the face.
12. *Maxillary Artery* is located on the side of the face.
13. *Lingual Artery* is located near the tongue.
14. *Carotid Artery* is located in the neck. This will supply blood to the skull, face and neck.

Note: Places where an artery supplies blood is usually part of the location for where the artery can be found.

Arteries of the Arm

1. *Axillary Artery* supplies blood to the shoulder, arm and chest.
2. *Ulnar Artery* supplies blood to the pinky side of hand.
3. *Radial Artery* supplies blood to the thumb side of hand.
4. *Brachial Artery* supplies blood to arm.

Arteries of the Leg

1. *Dorsalis Pedis Artery* supplies blood to the foot.
2. *Femoral Artery* supplies blood to the thigh.
3. *Posterior Tibial Artery* supplies blood to the foot and leg.

4. *Popliteal Artery* supplies blood to the knee.

Arteries of the trunk

1. *Internal Iliac Artery* supplies blood to the organs in the hip area and thigh areas.
2. *Common Iliac Artery* supplies blood around the stomach area.
3. *Aorta* branches into three new arteries above the heart which are the following: Brachiocephalic trunk, left common carotid artery, and left subclavian artery.
4. *Coronary Artery* supplies blood to the heart muscles.

Veins of the Head and Neck

1. *Facial Vein* receives blood from the face.
2. *Frontal Vein* receives blood from the forehead.
3. *Ophthalmic Vein* receives blood from the eyes.
4. *Superior Labial Vein* receives blood from the lips.
5. *Superior-Orbital Vein* receives blood form above eye.
6. *Jugular Vein* receives blood from the neck and face.

Veins of the arm

1. *Axillary Vein* receives blood from shoulder and brings it to the heart.
2. *Cephalic Vein* receives blood from thumb side of arm.
3. *Basilic Vein* receive blood from pinky side arm.

Veins of the leg

1. *Femoral Vein* receives blood from the thigh.
2. *Greater Saphenous Vein* receives blood from the big toe side of the leg. This is referred to as the medial side of the leg. This is the longest vein in the body.
3. *Lesser Saphenous Vein* receives blood from the back of the leg. The back of the leg in medical terminology is known as the posterior part of the leg.
4. *Popliteal Vein* receives blood from the veins in the lower leg. This vein is located in the knee area.

Veins of the Trunk

1. *Superior Vena Cava* receives most blood from the upper portion of the body, which is above the heart.

2. *Inferior Vena Cava* receives most blood from the lower portion of the body, which is below the heart.

3. *Coronary Vein* receives blood from the muscles of the heart.

4. *Common Iliac Vein* puts blood into inferior vena cava.

Circulation

Blood is always circulating in the arteries, veins and capillaries through out the body. Blood is what keeps the body warm. Before we describe circulation, the ingredients of **blood** will first be discussed. One component of blood is the **red blood cell**. Red blood cells are needed to bring oxygen from the lungs to the cells of the body. Red blood cells live in the body for 120 days. In addition, red blood cells are needed to bring carbon dioxide from the cells of the body to the lungs. When the carbon dioxide reaches the lungs, it goes out of the body whenever one exhales air (breathes out). Another component of blood is the **white blood cell** also called a *leukocyte*. White blood cells are needed in the blood to protect the body against disease. They are the essence of the body's immunity against disease. **Platelets** are another type of cell in the blood that is responsible for the clotting of blood. For example, when one gets a paper cut, platelets are responsible for the stopping the flow of blood. If a person did not have any platelets, a simple paper cut would keep on bleeding. This eventually would lead to death from the loss of blood. These cells described above are in the following order in increasing quantity in the blood:

White Blood Cells ------- Platelets -------- Red Blood Cells

In other words, there are more red blood cells in the blood than platelets and white blood cells. However, there are more platelets than white blood cells in the blood. The fluid part of the blood is called **plasma**. Most of the plasma is made of water, and a small amount of it is composed of proteins. Look at plasma as the liquid portion of the blood, and blood cells as the solid parts.

Hemopoiesis is the production of blood cells in the body.

Erythrocytes (pronounce e-rith-ro-sites) are also known as red blood cells. The best way to study the circulation of the blood through out the body is to study the heart blood flow. Deoxygenated blood from the head and neck or blood above the heart enters the superior vena cava. This large vein brings

blood to the top part of the right atrium of the heart. Also, deoxygenated blood from the stomach and legs or blood below the heart enters the inferior vena cava. This large vein brings blood to the bottom part of the right atrium of the heart. Now the deoxygenated blood in the right atrium enters the right ventricle of the heart. From there, the blood enters the pulmonary trunk, which will bring the blood to the lungs. In the lungs, this deoxygenated blood becomes oxygenated. Remember that the deoxygenated blood is full of wastes and carbon dioxide. This is released when one exhales. So when one inhales oxygen, it enters the lungs and gets into the blood. This type of blood is called oxygenated blood. The oxygenated blood returns to the heart by way of the left pulmonary vein. The oxygenated blood now enters the left atrium and then travels to the left ventricle. Finally the oxygenated blood leaves the heart by way of the aorta. In this way, the aorta will transport the blood to all parts of the body.

Diseases, Medical Terminology and Clinical Procedures

Hemophilia is a disease where the blood clots at a very slow rate. This is because of defective platelets. People with this condition are at risk of bleeding to death from a simple cut.

Dysrhythmia is an abnormal rhythm of the heart.

Palpitation is a symptom when one can feel their own heart beating. The heart feels like its fluttering.

Angiocardiography is a procedure where a dye is injected into the patient. Then the patient's heart is x-rayed. The dye makes the heart show better on x-ray. In this way, the doctor can make a more accurate diagnosis.

Cardiomegaly is an enlargement of the heart.

Tachycardia is an abnormally fast heartbeat. The normal average heartbeat is between 60 and 90 beats per minute. Tachycardia is usually over 100 beat per minute.

Bradycardia is an abnormally slow heartbeat.

Risk factors of heart disease consists of eating a high, meat based diet, lack of exercise, high blood pressure, smoking, and high emotional stress.

Arteriosclerosis is an abnormal condition of the arteries. The walls of the arteries get a buildup of fat, which can lead to high blood pressure and heart disease. Once again this condition can be reversible. Eliminating meat and dairy fat in the diet may reverse this condition.

VI. The Immune and the Lymphatic Systems

Structure and Function

Lymph is a clear or yellow fluid that contains many white blood cells and small amount of red blood cells. White blood cells serve as a defense against bacteria or viruses that the body might encounter.

Lymphatic System consists of the lymph fluid, lymph nodes, spleen, thymus, tonsils, bone marrow, and appendix. The lymphatic system is a primary part of the immune system.

Immune System consists of cells or substances in the body that protect us against disease. These cells or substances consists of the following:

1. *Lymphocytes* are types of white blood cells, which are the primary cells of the lymphatic system. B lymphocytes (B cells) and T lymphocytes (T Cells) are two types. B lymphocytes make antibodies. T lymphocytes function in immunity also. It is good to see the lymphatic and immune systems as related and act in each other's best interest. Patients with A.I.D.S. have low T lymphocyte counts (T cell counts). The less lymphocytes you have, the less defense against disease one has.

2. *Antibody* is a protein made by the B lymphocyte. It defends against foreign bacteria, viruses and parasites in the body. Foreign substances in the body that create an immune response are called antigens. Bacteria, poison, viruses and parasites are all types of antigens. Antigens react with antibodies. In other words, antibodies fight against the antigen. This is the whole process of the immune system.

3. *Macrophages* are large white blood cells that destroy bacteria (antigens) in the body. They do this by actually eating the bacteria, viruses, or other toxic substances.

4. *Neutrophils* are white blood cells that also eat bacteria. They have this in common with the macrophages. The eating of bacteria leads to the death of bacteria. When bacteria are eaten and digested by the neutrophil, pus will form. Sometimes pus is seen in minor cuts.

5. *Eosinophils* are types of white blood cells that fight against parasitic

worms in the body. These parasitic worms are sometimes attained by eating sushi, pork, and meat.

6.   *Basophils* are types of white blood cells that are important in inflammatory conditions. For example, when one strains his or her ankle, the ankle becomes inflamed. This is because basophils release chemicals that make the ankle swell. The swelling is the body's attempt to reduce or stop movement minutes after an injury. In this way, the sprained ankle can heal faster. Basophils also help in allergic reactions. When there are allergic reactions, there is usually inflammation present. For example, snake venom can cause many allergic reactions (with inflammation at place of bite) in many people. The body inflames the skin around the bite to try to prevent the poison from spreading to other parts of the body. You can guarantee that basophils will be working overtime in cases of snake bites.

Lymph nodes are oval in shape and are found around most of the body. Locations include some of the following: side of neck, back of neck, armpit, back of knee, legs and groin areas. Lymph nodes have concentrations of white blood cells that serve as immunity against disease. Lymph nodes also function as filters. They filter out any harmful bacteria or toxic substances in the lymph. In this way, lymph nodes can stop the spread of disease in the body. Sometimes lymph nodes get enlarged with certain types of cancers. This is a reason many doctors may check your lymph nodes during a routine medical exam.   Here are some names and locations of lymph nodes.

Name of Lymph Node	**Location**
1. *cervical lymph node*	*neck*
2. *femoral lymph node*	*thigh*
3. *tibial lymph node*	*leg*
4. *submandibular lymph node*	*under the jaw*
5. *occipital lymph node*	*top of the back of the neck*
6. *inguinal lymph node*	*groin*
7. *axillary lymph node*	*armpit*
8. *popliteal lymph node*	*in back of the knee*
9. *preauricular lymph node*	*in front of ear*

Tonsils are types of lymphatic tissue. Here are three types of tonsils which are the following: pharyngeal tonsil, palatine tonsil, and lingual tonsil. The pharyngeal tonsil is located in the nasopharynx (*refer back to respiratory*

system P. 17 on this structure). The palatine tonsil can be observed near the sides of the back of the tongue. The lingual tonsil is located at the back of the tongue. Tonsils are important for protection against bacteria.

Spleen is an organ found under the lower left side of the rib cage. It consists of lymphatic tissue and is 5 inches in length. It can be described as purple-like in color, and spongy. The spleen actually has two parts. The white pulp directly fights against any bacteria. The red pulp functions in getting rid of defective blood cells from the blood.

Bone Marrow is located in the skeleton where white blood cells, red blood cells and platelets are produced.

Thymus is located above the heart. Immature T lymphocytes go here from the bone marrow to mature and become regular T lymphocytes.

Appendix is a structure attached to the cecum (part of the large intestine) that has been considered to be involved in immune functions of the body.

Immunoglobulins are also known as antibodies. They fight against disease. There are five different types of the immunoglobulins in the body which are the following:

1. IgG is the most abundant type of immunoglobulin. It is located in the blood, intestines and lymph. It protects the body against viruses and bacteria. This is such a vital antibody for the fetus. This is because this is the only type of antibody that the mother can pass to the fetus (developing baby in the mother).

2. IgA is an immunoglobulin found in tears, saliva, mucous of small intestines, lymph and blood. It gives resistance against infection in the mucous membranes of the body.

3. IgM is an immunoglobulin that appears after first meeting or exposure to an antigen. For example, if someone never was exposed to a flu virus before, this immunoglobulin will be the first one to appear and respond to defending the body against attack from the virus. IgM also appears in lymph and blood.

4. IgD is an immunoglobulin found in lymph, blood, and on top of B lymphocytes. IgD is responsible for activating B lymphocytes to make more immunoglobulins (antibodies).

5. IgE is the least abundant type of immunoglobulin. It is involved with

allergic reactions. Some known allergens include the following: cow's milk, pollens, dust, snake venom, poison-ivy, bee stings.

Diseases, Medical Terminology, and Clinical Procedures

Splenomegaly is an enlarged spleen.

Lymphadenectomy is removal of the lymph node.

Phagocytosis is the process of eating or ingesting toxic substances in the body. Macrophages get rid of bacteria by the process of phagocytosis.

Lymphoma is a cancerous tumor of lymphatic tissue.

Hodgkin's disease is a type of cancer found in the lymph nodes. This disease usually occurs in men between the ages of 15 and 34 and senior citizens. Signs and symptoms include the following: weight loss, night sweats, and enlarged lymph nodes.

Complete Blood Count is a lab procedure which is done by analyzing a sample of a patient's blood. Generally, a complete blood count counts the number of white blood cells and red blood cells. High amounts of white blood cells can imply there are certain bacterial infections in the body. In this way, doctors can use this as a clue to a more accurate diagnosis.

Blood Transfusion is the medical procedure for transferring of blood from one person to another.

Purpura are blue and purple-like bruises sometimes found on the body.

Thrombocytopenia is a low amount of platelets in the blood.

Neutropenia is a decreased amount of neutrophils in the blood. Neutrophils protect us against bacterial infections. Some types of antibiotics can cause neutropenia.

Lymphocytopenia is a very low amount of lymphocytes in the blood. Cancer and A.I.D.S patients have low amounts of lymphocytes.

Leukemia is a cancer of the white blood cells.

Eosinophilia is a high amount of eosinophils in the blood. When eosinophilia occurs, you can suspect that the person is fighting a parasitic infection. Remember when eating sushi, you are at a greater risk of ingesting a parasite into your system. Some parasites can grow up to greater than 8 feet long in the intestines.

Mononucleosis is caused by the Epstein-Barr Virus. Symptoms include the following: enlarged spleen, fever, fatigue, fever, and enlarged lymph nodes in the neck area. This disease occurs mainly in teenagers and young adults. This disease is contagious.

HIV Positive means a patient has the antibodies for human immunodeficiency virus (HIV) present. Signs or symptoms consist of rapid weight loss, fever, and weakness. However, many patients can be HIV positive and never get A.I.D.S.

A.I.D.S. is referred to the acquired immune deficiency syndrome. A patient with this condition has a weakened immune system and is more susceptible to disease than people with a healthy or normal immune system. Diseases that most people never acquire are more likely for an A.I.D.S. patient. Rare cancers like Kaposi sarcoma are easily contracted. Also recurrent pneumonia is consistent with A.I.D.S patients. Other symptoms of A.I.D.S. include: weight loss, fever, fatigue and chronic diarrhea.

Congenital is something a patient is born with. For example, a person with congenital lymphedema is born with a underdeveloped lymphatic system, which will cause swelling of the arms and legs.

Elephantiasis is an extreme swelling of the legs, arms or other body part. There is an extreme lymphedema. However, in this case, this type of lymphedema is not congenital or something one is born with. This type of lymphedema is acquired through the bite of an infected mosquito. The mosquito transmits the parasitic worm called *Wuchereria bancrofti* into the patient. These parasitic worms will infect the lymph nodes. In this way, the lymph flow is blocked causing lymph to build up in the arms or legs, which causes the swelling. A patient afflicted with elephantiasis in the legs will actually resemble the thickness and shape of an elephant's leg. The legs become extremely thick, some almost as thick as small tree trunks. Elephantiasis occurs primarily in parts of Africa.

Beef Tapeworm is known in medical terminology as *Taenia saginata*. This tape worm is acquired by ingesting larvae of this worm in undercooked beef. The larvae mature in the intestines to become worms. In fact, it actually sticks to the inside walls of the intestines. It can grow to a length of more than 32 feet. Weight loss and malnutrition are signs of this infection.

Fish Tapeworm is known in medical terminology as *Diphyllobothrium latum*. It is acquired by eating the larvae of these worms in raw fish (salmon, trout). This tapeworm can grow to over 50 feet in length in the digestive system. This definitely doesn't sound appetizing.

Ophthalmoscope instrument for viewing the inner parts of the eye. It is commonly used by an ophthalmologist, which is an eye doctor.

VII. The Excretory System

Structure and Function

The excretory system has two primary functions:
1. *to remove waste products from the blood*
2. *to get rid of these waste products from the body*
If the body does not get rid of its waste products, these waste products will work as poison on the body. Waste products are toxic to the body.
Here are some waste products of the body:
-carbon dioxide (when we exhale)
-heat (from the skin)
-water
-sodium
-ammonia (found in urine)
-sulfate
-hydrogen

Skin, Kidneys, Lungs, Liver, Large Intestine

Skin gets rid of excess heat in the body, salt, water and carbon dioxide.
Kidneys excrete or get rid of water, toxins from bacteria, salts, heat, carbon dioxide and ammonia. There are two kidneys in the body. They are red-like in color and are found above the waist. They are about 5 inches long. The left kidney is usually higher than the right kidney. The left kidney is located on the patient's left side of the lower abdomen towards the back, and the right kidney is located on the patient's right side of the lower abdomen toward the back. The functional unit of the kidney is the nephron. Nephrons can only be seen under a microscope. Nephrons have the following three functions:
1. *Filtration*
2. *Secretion*
3. *Reabsorption*

With filtration, some substances in the blood are allowed to go into the nephrons in the kidney and some substances cannot enter. With secretion, the filtrated substances move more through the nephron and pick up additional wastes. With reabsorption, any materials picked up in the rest of

the nephron that are not wastes are returned back to the body by way of the blood. The wastes go out of the body in the form of urine. For a simple explanation, blood flow in the kidney occurs like this. Blood enters the renal artery, which goes into the kidney and the blood then comes out through the renal vein.

Ureters are tube-like structures that attach the kidneys with the urinary bladder. There is one ureter that attaches the left kidney with the urinary bladder. There is one ureter that attaches the right kidney with the urinary bladder.

Urinary Bladder is the place where urine is stored.

Urethra is a tube-like structure that attaches to the urinary bladder. The urethra is like a hose that lets the urine out of the body.

Lungs get rid of heat, water and carbon dioxide from the body.

Liver is the largest organ of the body. The liver is a wonderful organ because it gets rid of the toxicity of poisons in the body. For example, alcohol is neutralized by the liver so it doesn't kill us. However, if too much the poison is taken in by the body, the liver will be overworked and some instances overdose will kill a person. Alcohol is considered a poison. There is so many studies that link alcohol to throat, liver, esophagus and stomach cancer. If one thinks alcohol in moderation will prevent a heart attach, he or she are mistaken. There have been studies about drinking a glass of wine a day will lower the risk of heart attacks or heart disease. Well, it's actually the grapes in the wine that have this effect. There are antioxidants in grapes and other fruits and vegetables that can help prevent disease. Just have some grapes every day and one will find it more beneficial than drinking a glass of wine. The liver is also important for eliminating food additives in the diet. Eating too many of these additives will overwork the liver. The liver also makes bile which is a substance needed to digest fats in the body. Here are some other functions of this organ:

- changes carbohydrates and proteins into fat so it can be stored
- stores Vitamin A and Vitamin B
- it excretes bile by way of the small intestine
- it also destroys old red blood cells and excretes them by way of the small intestine

Large Intestine is made of the ascending colon, transverse colon, descending colon, and sigmoid colon. This organ absorbs water from the feces. In this way, the feces become a solid mass. The large intestine

excretes food wastes from the body.

Diseases, Medical Terminology and Clinical Procedures

<u>**Urinalysis**</u> is a medical procedure that examines the urine physically and chemically. Normal urine is usually clear and light yellow in color. Darker yellows can indicate dehydration or a lack of water in the body. When the urine sample is taken from the patient, a dipstick is placed in it. The dipstick is a chemical strip with different colors on it. Each color represents a different possible ingredient that is being tested for in the urine sample. Typically, the color will change when there is a certain substance present in the urine. The following is a list of substances tested for in a urinalysis.

1. *Protein* in the urine can be a sign of kidney disease. Of course, other medical tests would have to be performed before making such a diagnosis.

2. *Glucose* in the urine can indicate that a person has diabetes. Glucose is a sugar.

3. *Ketones* in the urine are substances that the body forms that can indicate the following: diabetes, alcohol intoxication, or the person is on a starvation diet. Ketones are produced when the body breaks down fat.

4. *Red Blood Cells* in the urine can indicate kidney stones or some kind of trauma. It can also be a normal finding. Typically, when one works out and lifts weights, blood will be found in the urine. Most blood found in the urine cannot be seen in the urine. It is in small quantities that only a chemical strip or microscope can observe.

5. *Nitrites* in the urine can detect a bacterial infection.

6. *White Blood Cells* in the urine in many cases indicate an urinary tract infection.

The urine is also tested for its physical characteristics. Here are the following characteristics:

1. *Color* of urine is a clue to finding the proper diagnosis. Color can be affected by the foods we eat. For example, ingestion of many beets will turn the urine a reddish color. Swallowing of B Vitamins will turn the urine a

light, bright greenish color. Urine has been found to be a variable number of colors including yellow, amber, red, green and even black.

2. *Volume* of urine is usually between 1 to 2 quarts per day for an adult.

3. *Odor* of urine will sometimes give clues to what one eats and the conditions one has. For example, a sweet odor to urine might indicate that a person is a diabetic. Normal odor of urine smells like ammonia a few to several hours after the sample has been taken.

4. *pH* is a measure of determining if a urine sample is acidic or basic. A pH below 7 is considered acidic, and a pH above 7 is considered basic. Normally, water should have a pH of 7, which is considered neutral. Meat eaters usually have urine with an acidic pH. Vegetarians usually have urine with a basic pH. You can tell a lot from someone's urine.

5. *Turbidity* means that the urine becomes cloudy after being collected. Urine should be clear enough where you can see through it. Most of urine is made of water. A small amount of urine is made of wastes.

Intravenous Urography is an x-ray technique used to visualize the kidneys and lower urinary tract. The patient is given a radiopaque substance intravenously (by needle) and then an x-ray is taken. This radiopaque substance will make the kidneys and other structures of the urinary tract more visible on x-ray. In this way, doctors can make a more precise diagnosis.

Cystogram is an x-ray picture of the bladder that was obtained using the technique of intravenous urography.

Ultrasound Scanning is a technique used to visual structures inside the body. Ultrasound uses sounds wave to produce an image on a monitor. Ultrasound can be used for viewing the kidneys, ureters, bladder, joints in the spine, joints in the hands to name a few. When ultrasound is used to view the joints, inflammation is what is being sought after. When it is used to view the kidneys and other urinary structures, kidney stones and other masses are sought after.

Computed Tomography (CT) is a medical procedure used to test for kidney tumors or other masses. CT can distinguish between what is solid and what is liquid. You can see how this technique would be very useful in

the bladder where a lot of liquid is typically found in the form of urine.

Cystitis is an inflammation of the urinary bladder usually caused by a bacterial infection. Symptoms include the following: painful urination, needing to urinate more often, and pain in the lower part of the spine.

Dysuria means painful urination.

Polyuria means urinating too much. This can happens with diabetic patients.

Urethritis is an inflammation of the urethra.

Enuresis is really another word meaning bed wetting. This occurs in infants and people with certain type of diabetes.

Incontinence is the uncontrollable escape of urine. This can occur by coughing, running, or laughing. This can also occur with certain diseases.

Hematuria refers to blood in the urine.

Glucosuria refers to glucose in the urine.

Proteinuria refers to protein in the urine.

Cytology is the study of cells.

Urine cytology is used to observe the cells in the urine under a microscope. The purpose of this is to screen for urinary tract cancers.

Nephritis is an inflammation of the kidneys. This is usually caused by a kidney infection.

Urinary Tract Infection or **UTI** is known as an infection of the urinary system with bacteria found in the urine.

Superior in medical terminology means toward the head. For example, the head is superior to the neck

Inferior means toward the feet. For example, the legs are inferior to the chest. The neck is inferior to the head. The bladder is inferior to the liver.

Posterior refers to the back portion of the body. The back is posterior to the chest.

Lumbar are bones in the lower spine that are located in the lower back.

Dorsal refers to the posterior portion of a body part.

Anterior refers to the front portion of the body. The chest is anterior to the back.

Micturition is the medical term for urination.

Volume of Urine the normal amount of urination in a 24 hour period is between 1 to 2 quarts per day.

Diuretics are drugs that cause the urine flow to increase.

Renal Calculi are known as kidney stones.

Shock Wave Lithotripsy is the medical procedure using sound waves to

break up large kidney stones into smaller ones.

Transitional Epithelium is a type of skin tissue that is found around the urinary bladder. It permits the bladder to stretch when it's full of urine.

VIII. The Nervous System

Divisions

The nervous system is made of two divisions, which consists of the central nervous system (CNS) and the peripheral nervous system (PNS).

Central Nervous System consists of the spinal cord and brain. It is important to visualize the spinal cord as an extension of the brain. The brain is the main circuit and the spinal cord is like an electric wire connected to it. Muscle contraction and gland secretion occur by nerve impulses from the central nervous system.

Peripheral Nervous System is made up of the spinal nerves that come from the spinal cord and cranial nerves that are connected to the brain. The cranial nerves are found in the head and upper neck area. It is important to realize that the central nervous system and the peripheral nervous system are connected. In this way, each system can send each other messages.

Sensory neurons are also known as afferent neurons, which are nerve cells. They carry impulses or messages from sense organs to the brain. Sensory neurons are part of the peripheral nervous system. In fact, the sensory neurons bring the messages from the peripheral nervous system to the central nervous system. For example, when one feels a hot stove, the message is sent from the hand to the brain by way of a nerve impulse. This nerve impulse (which is like electricity) tells the brain that the stove is hot by feeling the sensation of pain. Other sensations that are picked up by body in this way are the following: hearing, taste, heat, sight, touch, and cold.

Motor neurons are also known as efferent neurons, which are nerve cells. They carry impulses or messages from the brain to the muscles. Motor neurons are part of the peripheral nervous system. In fact, the motor neurons bring messages from the central nervous system to the peripheral nervous system. For example, the brain tells the arm to pick up an object. The message is sent from the brain by way of a nerve impulse. The nerve impulse (which is like electricity) moves the arm to perform the desired movement.

* The peripheral nervous system is divided into two different portions which are the following:

Somatic nervous system is made of somatic motor neurons that connects the central nervous system and skeletal muscles. This part of the peripheral nervous system is under conscious thought. In other words, it is voluntary.

Autonomic nervous system consists of sensory neurons that are mainly around the organs of the body. This part of the peripheral nervous system is involuntary. For example, the kidneys carry out its functions without thinking about it. The autonomic nervous system is involuntary. In addition, the autonomic nervous system is made of two parts, which consists of the following:

-*Sympathetic division* (fight-or-flight division) stimulates activities of the body when the body is under stressful situations good or bad. Energy of the body is used up at a faster pace when under sympathetic division influence. For example, high-adrenaline feelings (natural high or rush) are under sympathetic division influence. Another example, a bully at a school yard challenges a child half his size to a fight. Will the child half his size fight or run away (flight)? Well, either way, the sympathetic division takes over. The system protects us from harm or helps us be aggressive when we choose to be. Here are some effects of the sympathetic division:
1. Sweat increases in palms and soles of feet.
2. Break down of fat in the body.
3. Dilation or enlargement of the pupils of the eyes.
4. Decreases saliva in the mouth
5. Contraction of the muscles
6. Hair stands straight up.
7. Increase in heart beat
8. Blood pressure increases.

-*Parasympathetic division* stimulates the activities of the body to conserve energy. Generally, when one is relaxed, the person is under parasympathetic division influence. Here are some of the effects of this division:
1. Decrease in heart beat
2. Increases saliva
3. Inside of intestine relaxes
4. Increases motility of food in intestines

5. Erection of genital area in both sexes
6. Constriction (narrowing) of pupils in the eyes
7. Blood pressure decreases.

Nerve Tissue
(Neuroglia, Neurons, Synapses, Action Potentials, Myelination)

<u>Neurons</u> are nerve cells that conduct impulses. Neurons are the functional and structural cells of the nervous system. Without neurons, the nervous system doesn't exist. The neuron is composed of the following structures: *Cell Body* contains the nucleus, cytoplasm, mitochondria, lysosomes and golgi complex. Other synonyms for the cell body are soma and perikaryon.

Dendrites are branches that attach to the cell body. They are found practically around the whole cell body. Dendrites conduct nerve impulses toward the cell body. Dendrites like the cell body, also contain organelles.

Dendrite ——> cell body —> Nerve impulse

Axon is a structure that is connected to the cell body. The axon looks like a long tube. It is covered with a myelin sheath (fat covering). To sum up, nerve impulses go from the dendrites, to the cell body and finally the nerve impulse is conducted in the axon. To make this simpler think of it like this. The axon is like an electric wire that attaches to an outlet that is in a wall. The outlet would be the cell body. Inside the wall, this outlet attaches to other wires, which can be identified as the dendrites. The axon also has a cytoplasm called the axoplasm. At the end of an axon are structures called synaptic end-bulbs. Neurotransmitters are stored here (this will be explained later under synapsis in this chapter).

*Neurons come in three different physical types:
Multipolar Neurons are the most common type of neuron in the body. They contain many dendrites, one axon, and one cell body.
Bipolar Neurons have one dendrite and one axon.
Unipolar Neurons have only one process that extends from the cell body. This one process consists of a fusion of a dendrite and axon.

* Neurons come in two different functional types:
Efferent Neurons conduct motor nerve impulses from the spinal cord and brain to the glands and muscles.

ME

Afferent Neurons conduct nerve impulses from the sense organs, skin, and muscles to the spinal cord and brain.

Neuroglia are smaller in size than neurons. Neuroglia are part of the nervous system; they give support and nutrition to the neurons. There are at least 10 times more neuroglia than neurons in the body. The following cells are types of neuroglia:

Ependymal cells are part of the central nervous system. Ependymal cells are epithelial cells found around the spinal cord and brain.

Astrocytes are star-shaped cells found in the central nervous system. They function in connecting neurons with blood vessels. They also help in keeping potassium levels within normal limits so the nerves can conduct impulses to contract muscles. For example, bananas have a large amount of potassium. Potassium helps with muscle contraction.

Oligodendrocytes (pronounced ol-i-go-den-dro-sites) are cells that resemble astrocytes but are smaller in size. Oligodendrocytes are located in the central nervous system. They give needed support to neurons. They help make a lining around neurons. This lining is made of fat. This lining is called a myelin sheath. This myelin sheath or lining of fat is needed to conduct nerve impulses. If you can't conduct impulses, muscles won't move properly and the body would be uncoordinated. Infants lack coordination because their myelin sheaths are not fully matured. Myelin sheaths also help to conduct nerve impulses at a fast rate. Sometimes fat in the body has good purposes. In other words, a certain level of fat in the body is needed for survival.

Microglia (pronounced mi-krog-lee-a) are cells that are found in the central nervous system. Microglia eat any bacteria in the central nervous system that shouldn't be there (phagocytosis).

Schwann cells *(also called Neurolemmocytes)* are found in the peripheral nervous system. They make myelin sheaths or fat lining around neurons in the peripheral nervous system.

Satellite cells are found in the peripheral nervous system. They help support neurons. Satellite cells are found around neurons.

Synapses mostly are junctions or small little bridges between neurons. These junctions serve as a way of relaying messages from neuron to neuron. In this way, one neuron conducts a nerve impulse and gives it to the next neuron by way of a synapse. Then the next neuron gives its nerve impulse to the next neuron by way of a synapse. Finally, when the nerve impulse from neurons in the brain reach the neurons in a body part, then the body part can move and perform a specific action. There are two kinds of synapses which consists of the following:

1. *Electrical Synapses* allow for faster communication between neurons. This allows for faster nerve conduction. They are faster than chemical synapses. This is because neurons have bridges or junctions between them. In other words, they are connected.

2. *Chemical Synapses* allow slower communication between neurons. This is because there is an opening between neurons but with no bridge or junction. This is referred to as the synaptic cleft. Actually, they have special chemicals called neurotransmitters that transmit messages from neuron to neuron. The neurotransmitter has to travel much like a ship in water from one neuron to another. This allows for slower nerve conduction.

Action Potentials are referred to as nerve impulses. Action potentials are created by the natural occurring voltage in the body. The membrane around neuron called the plasma membrane has little holes for ions to enter. The plasma membrane is composed of fat so to let the voltage flow easier. These ions are electrically charged. The ions come in the form of mainly potassium (K^+), sodium (Na^+), and calcium (Ca^+). Now these electrically charged positive ions come in from the outside of the neuron through the tiny holes of the plasma membrane to get inside the neuron. However, there are electrically charged negative ions inside the neuron. These negative ions attract the positive ions to get inside the neuron. Remember with electricity negative always attracts positive. The voltage inside the neurons is measured in millivolts (mV). Before the positive ions entered, the voltage inside the neuron was -70 mV. The neuron was in a state of rest called the resting membrane potential. Now when the positive ions enter, the voltage inside the neuron is +5 mV. Soon after, the voltage inside the neuron goes back to -70 mV. The changing from -70 mV to +5 mV and then back again to -70 mV makes up when the action potential (nerve impulse) occurs. The whole action potential occurs for less than 1/1000th of a second. This nerve

impulse can then let a muscle perform the desired action. It actually does take electrical voltage to move muscle.

Myelination refers to the axons being surrounded by a myelin sheath or lining of fat. This myelin sheath raises the speed of nerve conduction.

Spinal Cord and Brain/Cranial Nerves

Spinal Cord is oval in shape. It extends from the lowest part of the brain called the medulla and ends in the lower back area. It ends approximately at lumbar vertebra 2 (see P. 50). The total length of the spinal cord is approximately 17 inches and almost 1 inch in diameter. At lumbar vertebra 2 the spinal cord becomes like a point of a cone. This is referred to as the *conus medullaris* (pronounced med-yoo-Lar-is). Around the spinal cord and brain are connective tissue coverings called meninges. There are three types of meninges which are the following:
1. *Pia Mater* is the innermost covering of the brain and spinal cord.
2. *Arachnoid* is the middle covering of the brain and spinal cord.
3. *Dura Mater* is the outermost covering of the brain and spinal cord.

The inner structure of the spinal cord consists of sections called gray matter and white matter. Gray matter and white matter consists of different types of neurons that conduct nerve impulses to different parts of the body.

Spinal Nerves are indirectly attached to the spinal cord. There are 31 spinal nerves. The spine is named for each section of the back. The cervical area or neck area consists of 8 cervical nerves. The thoracic area is located from the bottom of the neck to the upper portion of the lower back. There are 12 thoracic nerves. The lumbar area starts inferior to the thoracic area. The lumbar area is known as the low back. There are five lumbar nerves. Below the lumbar area is the sacral part of the spine. The sacral area has five sacral nerves. Finally, below the sacral area is the coccyx. The coccygeal area has one coccygeal nerve. To sum up:
* 31 spinal nerves on each side of the spine
* 8 cervical nerves
* 12 thoracic nerves
* 5 lumbar nerves
* 5 sacral nerves

* 1 coccygeal nerve

Cranial Nerves are located in the brain. Each has a specific function. Some are motor, which create movements and some are sensory, which give information to our senses. In addition, some are both sensory and motor; these are called mixed cranial nerve. There are 12 cranial nerves which are the following:

1. Olfactory Nerve (Cranial Nerve I) is a sensory nerve that functions in giving one a sense of smell. For example, smelling the scent of coffee is a function of this nerve.

2. Optic Nerve (Cranial Nerve II) is a sensory nerve that functions for vision. This nerve is responsible for reading words on paper and all visual field perception (i.e. peripheral vision).

3. Oculomotor Nerve (Cranial Nerve III) is a motor nerve. This nerve is responsible for raising the eyelid, various movements of the eyeball, constriction of pupil, and for changing the shape of the eye lens in back of the eye. The movements of the eyeball that are controlled by the oculomotor nerve are the following:
-down and out
-medial (towards the nose)
-up and in
-up and out

4. Trochlear Nerve (Cranial Nerve IV) is a motor nerve. It moves the eyeball down and in.

5. Trigeminal Nerve (Cranial Nerve V) is a mixed nerve. It is both sensory and motor. It is made of three parts (trigeminal). Basically, most of the face is supplied by this nerve. Parts of the face specifically supplied by the nerve include the following: parts of the eyeball, forehead, skin on the face, tongue, teeth, inside the cheeks, and eyelids. This sensory portion conveys the sensation of touch, heat and pain. The motor portion of this nerve is for chewing.

6. Abducens Nerve (Cranial Nerve VI) is a motor nerve. It basically moves the eyeball directly lateral (towards the ear).

7. **Facial Nerve (Cranial Nerve VII)** is a mixed nerve. Its sensory portion is for the sensation of taste. The specific tastes that the facial nerve is responsible for is sweet, sour, and salty. Its motor portion is for facial expressions. Frowning, closing the eyes tightly, and smiling are a few facial expressions that the facial nerve is responsible for.

8. **Vestibulocochlear Nerve (Cranial Nerve VIII)** is also called the acoustic nerve. This nerve is sensory only. It is responsible for hearing and one's equilibrium (maintaining one's balance.)

vestibulo

9. **Glossopharyngeal Nerve (Cranial Nerve IX)** is a mixed nerve. Its motor portion is responsible for swallowing and sound from the voice box. Its sensory portion is responsible for the taste of bitter.

10. **Vagus Nerve (Cranial Nerve X)** is mixed nerve. Its motor portion is for sounds of speech and swallowing. Its sensory portion is for sensation in the ear canal.

11. **Spinal Accessory Nerve (Cranial Nerve XI)** is a motor nerve. It shrugs the shoulder and turns the head from side to side.

12. **Hypoglossal Nerve (XII)** is a motor nerve. It moves the tongue from side to side and it helps in swallowing.

Sensory-Motor System and Special Senses

Translation is when the nerve impulse is translated into a sensation.

Sense Organ is a type of neuron or sensory receptor that is in tune with changes that occur inside or outside the body.

Stimulus is a change in the outer environment of the body. A stimulus can turn on neurons.

Sensation is the conscious or unconscious knowing of a certain stimuli. All of the following are types of sensations:
1. pain
2. pressure
3. position
4. hearing
5. taste

6. touch

Sensory System consists when there is a certain stimulus that will bring on nerve impulses in sensory nerve fibers. The nerve impulse will then go back to the brain where this impulse is changed into a sensation.

Motor System conveys motor impulses from the brain to the muscles of the body. In this way, specialized movements can be performed. For example, bending the legs and arms are caused by motor impulses from the brain to the muscles in these extremities.

Perception is the conscious analysis of sensations.

Special Senses include the following: smell, vision, taste, hearing, and equilibrium.

Smell is an olfactory sensation. It is a chemical sense.

Taste is a gustatory sensation. It is a chemical sense.

Vision is a visual sensation.

Hearing is an auditory sensation.

Equilibrium is a sensation for balance.

Disorders, Injuries, Medical Terminology and Clinical Procedures

Tinnitus is a ringing in the ears. This is caused by injury to the vestibulocochlear nerve (cranial nerve eight).

Vertigo is a sensation where the room around the patient seems to be spinning. This is caused by injury to the vestibulocochlear nerve (cranial nerve eight).

Cyanosis bluish color of the skin from a lack of oxygen in the blood.

Meningitis is a condition that is characterized by an inflammation of the meninges (pia mater, arachnoid, dura mater). It can be bacterial, chronic, or viral. Bacterial meningitis is most commonly caused by streptococcus pneumoniae, a type of bacterium. Risk factors of acquiring bacterial meningitis for an adult is alcoholism, splenectomy (surgical removal of spleen), and pneumonia. However, bacterial meningitis is most common in infants between the ages of one and two. Symptoms of meningitis include the following: stiff neck, cyanosis, and neck pain. Chronic meningitis can be caused by the A.I.D.S. virus, syphilis or Lyme Disease. Viral meningitis can be caused by A.I.D.S., herpes and mumps. Meningitis can also be caused by brain tumors.

Brudzinski's Test is an orthopedic procedure used by health care providers. The patient lies on his or her back on the exam table. The examiner flexes

the patient's head to their chest. If the patient has neck pain or flexion of the knees when doing this procedure, the test would be positive for meningitis. It does not mean that a patient who tests positive for this test definitely has meningitis. In other words, this test with other medical procedures would confirm the diagnosis of meningitis. The good health care provider uses different exams and blood tests to screen for a specific condition. Relying on just one test to make a diagnosis in most cases is irresponsible, negligent and careless.

Multiple Sclerosis (M.S.) is a disease where demyelination occurs around the neurons. Neurons start to lose their myelin, which can lead to severe loss in muscle coordination. Symptoms and signs of multiple sclerosis include the following: numbness, tingling in the legs and arms, dropping objects involuntarily, decreased sexual sensation, which may inhibit orgasm and loss of vision. This condition usually first occurs in women between the ages of 20 and 40, and it does run in families. For some reason, people who live close to the equator are less affected with M.S.

Baragnosis is the inability to make a distinction between different weights of objects.

Chief Complaint is part of the patient's history. The chief complaint is the reason the patient comes to the doctor's office; it is in the patient's words. For example, a patient's chief complaint may be the following: "I have an achy pain around the eyes and keeps me up all night." After the patient writes his or her chief complaint, the doctor follows it up in series of questions. The questions are in the form of the following:

Onset - is when the pain headache started.

Provoking or Palliative - refers to what makes the headache or condition better or worse.

Quality - is the character of the pain. The doctor would ask if the pain is pounding, achy, or burning and to what extent.

Radiation - refers to whether the pain radiates to other places of the body or does it stay localized (stays in one place).

Site - refers to where the exact point of pain is. The doctor would ask where is the exact point of pain. In this case, the patient would point to the pain around his eyes.

Timing - refers to how often does the pain occur. The doctor may also ask is the pain constant or does it come and go.

After each question, the doctor will write the answers down on the patient's history. This is used for a form of documentation in many worker's

compensation and personal injury cases. Lastly, these history notes are used for assessing the patient's health for subsequent visits and as clues for making a diagnosis.

Bell's Palsy is a weakness of cranial nerve seven (facial nerve). This usually affects only one side of the face. Symptoms include the following: drooping eyelid, loss of taste, facial muscles become distorted on one side. It looks as if one side of the face is lower than the other side. Strokes and brain tumors can cause such a condition. However, sometimes this condition can come about without any known cause.

Ptosis (pronounced toe-sis) refers to a drooping eyelid. This can result from injury to the oculomotor nerve (cranial nerve three).

Trigeminal neuralgia is a condition, which results from injury to the trigeminal nerve (cranial nerve five). The patient would experience extreme pain most commonly in the cheek and jaw areas. The pain is a stabbing, piercing pain. The cause is sometimes by compression of cranial nerve five by an artery in the face. However, most causes of this condition are unknown.

Agnosia is the loss in the sense of smell. This is can occur by injury to the olfactory nerve (cranial nerve one).

Neuralgia is pain along a sensory nerve.

Glossopharyngeal Neuraglia is caused by injury to the cranial nerve nine where the person gets extreme pain in the throat.

IX. The Muscular/Skeletal System

Structure and Function
Bones And Muscles

Skeletal System is made of two parts, which are the axial skeleton and the appendicular skeleton. There are 206 bones in the body. The skeleton protects and supports the organs of the body. The skeleton along with muscles coordinate movement in the body to perform a physical action. For organizational purposes, axial skeleton will be discussed first.

Axial Skeleton consists of the following bones.

8 cranial bones
(1) frontal bone found in the forehead.
(2) parietal bones located on the sides of the back of the head.

(2) temporal bones located around both ears.

(1) occipital bone located in the lower back of the head.

(1) sphenoid bone located in front on both temporal bones and in the middle of the base of the skull. This bone looks like it has wings. It is peculiar in shape since most bones of the skull are flat. This is mostly an inner bone of the skull.

(1) ethmoid bone is found in back of and between the eyes. It is very important in our sense of smell.

14 Facial Bones

(2) nasal bones form the bridge of the nose.

(2) zygomatic bones are the cheek bones.

(2) maxillae bones are bones above the mouth. They are connected to almost every bone of the face except the mandible.

(2) palantine bones are L-shaped. They are found in the back portion of the roof of the mouth.

(2) inferior nasal conchae are bones located in the inner nose. They help in the filtration of air to the lungs.

(1) vomer forms the posterior portion of the nasal septum. The nasal septum is found in back of the nose.

(1) mandible, which is the jaw bone.

(2) lacrimal bones are the smallest bones of the face. They are found lateral (towards in the direction of the ears) and posterior to the nasal bones.

Vertebral Column (Spine)

Approximately 40% a person's height is made up of the spine. The vertebral column (spine) is composed of bones called vertebrae, which serve to protect the spinal cord from injury. The vertebrae can help in flexing, rotating and extending the spine. Muscles of the back are attached to these vertebrae. There are 26 vertebrae in the normal adult, which are the following.

Cervical Vertebrae

There are 7 cervical vertebrae. Cervical vertebrae start at the bottom of the back of the head to the top of the back. Cervical vertebrae are smaller than other vertebrae of the spine. The first cervical vertebrae is called C1 which starts at the bottom of the back of the head. The second cervical vertebrae is called C2 and is right below C1. Between each vertebra in the spine are

discs, which contain cartilage. These discs act as shock absorbers so when one walks or runs the vertebrae don't jam into one another. The first disc is between C2 and C3. On each vertebra in the spine are bones that stick out of them called spinous processes. These spinous processes are the bumps that you can feel in the middle of the back of the neck and back.

Thoracic Vertebrae
There are 12 thoracic vertebrae in the spine. Thoracic means pertaining to the chest. The first thoracic vertebra (T1) is found right below C7, which is at the bottom of the neck. The 12th thoracic vertebra (T12) is located on the top of the lower back.

Lumbar Vertebrae
There are 5 lumbar vertebrae in the spine. The first lumbar vertebra L1 is located right below T12. The 5th lumbar vertebra (L5) is located at the bottom of the lower back

Sacrum
There are 5 sacral segments that fuse into one bone called the sacrum. The sacrum can move as a unit. However, each individual sacral segment cannot move. Cervical, thoracic and lumbar vertebrae can move.

Coccyx
There are 4 coccygeal segments that fuse into one bone called the coccyx. The coccyx is referred to as the tailbone. Each coccygeal segment cannot move.

Hyoid Bone is a bone that does not connect with any other bone of the body. It sits in front of the 3rd cervical vertebra (C3). The hyoid bone is an attachment for muscles of the throat and gives support to the tongue.

Sternum is referred to as the breastbone, which is located in the center of the chest. It's about 5 to 6 inches in length. The sternum is made of three parts which are the following:
1. *Manbrium* is the upper portion of the sternum.
2. *Body* is the middle and lowers parts of sternum. This is the largest part of the sternum. It connects to the ribs. The medical term for two bones connecting at a point to make a joint is called an articulation.

3. Xiphoid process (pronounced Zi-foyd) is the smallest portion of the sternum. It is found at the lowest tip of the sternum. The xiphoid process is cartilage until it ossifies (becomes bone) by age 42.

Ribs in the body connect with the vertebra in the back. Ribs serve as a form of protection for the organs in the chest. Ribs also can also expand the trunk during breathing. The ribs connect with the sternum in the front or anterior part of the body. There are 12 ribs on the left side of the body and 12 ribs on the right side of the body.

Appendicular skeleton consists of the following bones.

Clavicle is the long bone that extends from the top of the sternum to the shoulder. There are two clavicles on each side of the body. The clavicles are the collarbones.

Scapula is the flat bone located in the back area. It is known as the shoulder blade. There are two scapulae.

Humerus is a bone that starts around the elbow and ends at the shoulder. The humerus connects with the ulna, which is one of the bones of the forearm.

Ulna is a bone of the forearm (lower arm). It connects (articulates) with the humerus and the bone next to it is called the radius. The ulna is on the pinky side of the forearm.

Radius is a bone of the forearm. It connects (articulates) with the ulna. The radius is on the thumb side of the forearm.

Carpals make up 8 small bones of the lower portion of the hand. The scaphoid, which is a carpal articulates with a portion of the radius.

Metacarpals are located in the upper part of the hand. There are a total of 10 metacarpals. Each hand has 5 metacarpals and each corresponds to each finger.

Phalanges refer to bones of the fingers or toes. They are directly connected

to the metacarpals of the hand or metatarsals of the foot. The first phalange is the thumb and the fifth phalange is the pinky. The first phalange of the foot is the big toe and the fifth phalange is the little toe.

Femur is the longest bone in the body. This is referred to as the thigh bone. It is connects (articulates) with the hip bone, tibia, and patella (knee bone).

Patella is the knee bone. It articulates with the femur.

Tibia is the shinbone. It articulates with the femur. There is a disc of cartilage between the femur and tibia. This prevents the bones from rubbing together. This disc is referred to as the meniscus.

Fibula is located on the lateral part of the shin. It articulates with the tibia (near the knee) and the talus of the foot.

Talus bones are referred to as the ankle bones. There are a total of seven tarsal bones which are the following: calcaneus, cuboid, talus, navicular, medial cuneiform, intermediate cuneiform, lateral cuneiform.

Metatarsal Bones are located in the foot. There are a total of 10 metatarsals. Each foot has five metatarsals and corresponds to each toe.

Hip Bone is also known as the pelvic bone. There is a right and left hip bone. The hip bone articulates with the sacrum and the femur. The hip bone consists of three parts which are the following:
ilium- is the upper portion of the hip. There is a right ilium on the right side of the hip and a left ilium on the left side of the hip.
pubis- is the front lower portion of the hip. There is a right pubis on the right side of the hip and a left pubis on the left side of the hip.
ischium- is the back lower portion of the hip. There is a right ischium on the right side of the hip and a left ischium on the left side of the hip. This is the bone that we sit on.

Muscular System supports and covers the skeleton. Muscles also give the body shape. The skeletal and nervous system are what helps move muscles. There are over 600 muscles in the body. Each muscle is supplied by a specific nerve. The nerve tells the muscle what movement to perform. The

nerve supply to a muscle is called the muscle's innervation. For example, the biceps muscle is innervated by the musculocutaneous nerve. In other words, it means that the biceps muscle has a nerve supply of the musculocutaneous nerve.

Muscles of the Face and Head
-Risorius brings the corners of the mouth back. It has a nerve supply of the facial nerve (cranial nerve 7). This muscle is found in the cheek area.
-Mentalis raises the chin. It has a nerve supply of the facial nerve. This muscle is found on the bottom of chin.
-Orbicularis Oculi is a circular muscle located around the eye. It closes the eye. It has a nerve supply of the facial nerve.
-Chewing muscles consists of the masseter, temporalis, medial pterygoid (pronounced TER-i-goid), and lateral pterygoid. These muscles are around the jaw and help in chewing food. They all have a nerve supply of the trigeminal nerve (cranial nerve 5).

Muscles of the Eyeballs
There are six eyeball muscles, which move the eyeballs in different directions consist of following:
- Inferior rectus, superior rectus, medial rectus and inferior oblique are innervated by cranial 3.
- Superior oblique is innervated by cranial nerve 4. This muscle moves the eyeball down and in.
- Lateral rectus is innervated by cranial nerve 6. This muscle moves the eye lateral in the direction of the ear.

Muscles of the Neck
-Sternocleidomastoid (SCM) rotates the neck to right or left. It has a nerve supply of the spinal accessory nerve (cranial nerve 11). This muscle is attached to the sternum and clavicle. There are 2 SCM muscles in the neck: one the right side of the neck and one on the left side.
-Digastric muscle depresses the jaw and raises the hyoid bone. There is one located on the left side of the neck and one the right side.
-(3) Scalene muscles rotate and flex the neck. These muscles are attached to the cervical vertebrae.

Muscles of the Chest

-(2) Pectoralis major muscles are found on each side of the chest. These muscles are attached to sternum, clavicle and upper ribs. They are responsible for adducting (bringing arm to midline or center of the body) and flexing the arm. The pectoralis muscle has a nerve supply of the medial and lateral pectoral nerves.

- Serratus anterior is a muscle found on the both sides of the trunk. It assists in breathing by raising the ribs

-Diaphragm is the main muscle of breathing. It has a nerve supply of the phrenic nerve. It is connected to the xiphoid process of the sternum.

Muscles of the abdomen

-Rectus Abdominis flexes the vertebral column and compresses the abdomen. It also helps in forced expiration. It has a nerve supply of the thoracic nerves. It is attached to the pubis (lower hip) and to ribs 5, 6 and 7.

-Transversus Abdominis compresses the abdomen. It is attached to the top of the hip. It has a nerve supply of the thoracic nerve.

-Internal Oblique compresses the abdomen and bends the vertebral column laterally (towards the side). It is attached to the top of the hip and to the bottom four ribs. It has a nerve supply of the thoracic nerve.

-External Oblique compresses the abdomen and bends the vertebral column laterally. It is attached to the lower eight ribs and the top of the hip.

Muscles of the Back

-Trapezius elevates the clavicle (collarbone), brings the scapula upward and downward, and extends head. The trapezius is attached to the clavicle, scapula, thoracic and cervical vertebrae. It has a nerve supply of the accessory nerve (cranial nerve 11). This muscle is located in the back of the neck and mid portion of the back.

-Latissimus Dorsi extends arm and brings arm downward and backward. This muscle is used primarily when climbing a mountain or wall. The latissimus dorsi is attached to thoracic vertebrae, lumbar vertebrae, sacrum, ilium and humerus. It has a nerve supply of the thoracodorsal nerve. This muscle is located on the both sides of the back from mid to lower back areas.

-Rhomboid muscles are located in the middle portion of the back. It draws shoulder blades posterior and upward. It has nerve supply of the dorsal scapula nerve.

-Erector Spinae muscles are found in the cervical, thoracic and lumbar areas of the spine. These muscles are responsible for extending the spine.

-Gluteus maximus is the largest muscle of the buttocks. It extends the thigh and rotates the thigh laterally. It is attached to the hip and femur. It has a nerve supply of the inferior gluteus nerve.

Muscles of the Arms

-Deltoid muscle is made of three parts (anterior, posterior, and lateral) and is located in the shoulder area. It extends, flexes and raises arms laterally to above the ears. It has a nerve supply of the axillary nerve.

-Biceps Brachii flexes the arm at the elbow. It has a nerve supply of the musculocutaneous nerve. It is made of up of two parts.

-Brachialis flexes the arm. It is found around the biceps brachii. It is attached to the humerus and ulnar. It has a nerve supply of the musculocutaneous nerve.

-Triceps brachii extends the arm. It is made of up three parts. It has a nerve supply of the radial nerve. It attaches to the scapula, humerus and ulnar.

-Anconeus (pronounced an-ko-ne-us) extends the arm. This muscle is much smaller than the triceps brachii. It is found in the upper portion of the forearm. This muscle is well-developed in tennis players. It is attached to the humerus and ulna. It has a nerve supply of the radial nerve.

-Extensor Carpi Ulnaris extends the hand and wrist. It is attached to the fifth metacarpal and the humerus. It has a nerve supply of the radial nerve.

-Flexor Carpi Ulnaris flexes or bends the hand. It is attached to the humerus and carpals of hand (lower portion of hand). It has a nerve supply of the ulnar nerve.

Muscles of the Legs

-Gluteus Medius brings legs together. It attaches to the hip and femur. It has a nerve supply of the superior gluteal nerve.

-Rectus Femoris, Vastus Lateralis, Vastus Medialis, Vastus Intermedius are known as the **quadricep** muscles. They are found on the front portion of the leg. They all extend the thigh. They have a nerve supply of the femoral nerve.

-Biceps femoris, semitendinosus, semimembranosus are known as the **hamstring** muscles. The hamstrings are located in the back of the leg. They flex the thigh and also extend the leg. They have a nerve supply of the tibial nerve.

-Sartorius is the longest muscle in the body. It is found on the inner portion of the thigh. It is not a hamstring muscle. The sartorius has a nerve supply of the femoral nerve. This muscle flexes the leg and rotates the leg inward. It is attached to the hip and the tibia.

-Gastrocnemius is a muscle located in the back of the lower portion of the leg. It plantar flexes the foot and flexes the leg. Plantar flexion of the feet can be demonstrated by walking on your toes. This muscle is supplied by the tibial nerve.

-Soleus is a muscle located a little lower (or inferior) than the gastrocnemius on the back of the leg. It also serves to plantar flex the foot. It has nerve supply of the tibial nerve.

-Tibialis Anterior is a muscle that dorsiflexors the foot. Dorsiflexion of the foot can be demonstrated by walking on your heals. This muscle is found on the front portion of the shin. It has a nerve supply of the deep peroneal nerve.

Muscles of the Feet
-Extensor Digitorium Brevis extends the toes. It has a nerve supply of the deep peroneal nerve.

-Flexor Digitorium Brevis flexes the toes. It has a nerve supply of the medial plantar nerve.

-Flexor Hallucis Brevis flexes only the big toe. It has a nerve supply of the medial plantar nerve.

Injuries, Medical Terminology and Clinical Procedures

Synarthrosis is an immovable joint in the body. Teeth would be an example of a synarthosis.

Amphiarthosis is a slightly moveable joint. The intervertebral discs (discs between the vertebrae) are examples.

Diathrosis is a freely moveable joint. Most joints of the body are of this type. The knee joint is an example of a diathrosis. There are six types of diathroses, which consist of the following:

1. Gliding joint (Example: the clavicle glides on the sternum.) Gliding refers to a side to side movement.

2. Ball-and-Socket joint allows flexion, extension, rotation, abduction (brings body part away from the center of the body), and adduction. Hip and should joints are ball-and-socket joints.

3. Hinge joint allows for flexion and extension. The elbow joint is a hinge joint.

4. Pivot joint allows for rotation. The joint between the first and second cervical vertebrae is a pivot joint.

5. Saddle joint allows for left to right, up and down, and circular movement. The bottom of the thumb consists of this type of joint. Try moving the thumb using its saddle joint movements.

6. Ellipsoidal joint or condyloid joint allows flexion, extension, abduction, adduction and circular movement. The wrist joint is a type of ellipsoidal joint.

Open Fracture is where a bone is fractured and goes through the outer skin. An open fracture is also called a compound fracture.

Closed Fracture is where a bone is fractured and does not go through the outer skin. A closed fractured is also called a simple fracture.

R.I.C.E. refers to the rest, ice, compression and elevation. This is the treatment method for many musculoskeletal injuries. Many health care providers use this method in the acute phase of injury, which is between the time of injury and first 24 hours after the injury.

Supination is the movement of turning the palm up towards the sky.

Pronation is the movement of turning the palm down towards the floor.

Circumduction is moving a body part in a circular type of motion. For example, the leg can perform circumduction since it is connected to the hip joint.

Adduction to bring a part of the body toward the center or midline of the body.

Abduction to bring a part of the body away from the center or midline of the body.

Myopathy is a disease of muscle.

Myositis is an inflammation of muscle.

Fibromyalgia is a chronic, painful muscle syndrome characterized by multiple tender points around the muscles of the body. This occurs mostly in women that are middle-aged. There are symptoms are tiredness, stiffness of joints and stiffness of muscles.

X. The Endocrine System

Glands, Hormones, and Body Regulation

Endocrine System consists of the endocrine glands in the body. However, there are two types of glands in the body. The exocrine glands or duct glands (not part of endocrine system) have ducts that lead to a particular body part. Exocrine glands are found in the skin and intestines. The endocrine glands or ductless glands secrete hormones, which are put directly into the bloodstream. The nervous system helps in releasing hormones from the glands. Hormones help to regulate metabolism in the body, helps in certain parts of the immune and reproductive system, aids in the regulation of smooth and cardiac muscle contraction and regulates growth and development.

Hypothalamus is an endocrine gland that serves as a communication link between the nervous and endocrine systems. The nervous systems sends messages to the endocrine system telling it what to do and what hormones to secrete. For example, the hypothalamus releases inhibiting hormones to the pituitary gland. In this way, this stops the releasing hormones of the pituitary gland. The releasing hormones are what stimulates certain hormones to be released from the pituitary gland.

Pituitary Gland (Hypophysis) is called the master gland. This gland is located in the brain and is the size of a kernel of corn. This gland produces hormones that regulates some processes of the body. There is an anterior pituitary gland called the anterior lobe (adenohypophysis) and a posterior pituitary gland called the posterior lobe. The anterior pituitary gland releases hormones which are the following:
1. *Somatotrophs* are cells that make human growth hormone. Human growth hormone regulates the growth of the muscles, bones and organs of the body.
2. *Corticotrophs* are cells that make melanocyte-stimulating hormone, which is responsible for a person's skin color.
3. *Lactotrophs* are cells that produce prolactin, which helps in the milk lactation in females.
4. *Gonadotrophs* produce follicle stimulating hormone, which helps in the production of the egg in the female and sperm in the male. Gonadotrophs

also aid in the production of estrogen in the female.

5. *Thyrotrophs* make the thyroid stimulating hormone (TSH), which regulates the thyroid gland.

The posterior pituitary gland does not make hormones. It only stores and releases hormones which are the following:

1. *Oxytocin* is a hormone that contracts the uterus during pregnancy and for milk let-down for the lactating female. The hypothalamus produces oxytocin and it is stored in the posterior pituitary until it is released.

2. *Antidiuretic Hormone* lowers the volume of urine. It is necessary for the body to lower the production of urine when the body is dehydrated. In this way, the water that was going to be excreted as urine will return into the blood of the body. This is a way of conserving precious water needed by the body. It also can raise blood pressure especially when one loses large amounts of blood in a short period of time. The hypothalamus produces antidiuretic hormone and it is stored in the posterior pituitary until it is released.

Thyroid Gland is an endocrine gland located below the larynx or voice box. The thyroid weighs only about 1 to 2 ounces. It has a left lateral lobe and right lateral lobe. These lobes are connected by a structure called the isthmus. The whole gland consists of tiny sacs called thyroid follicles. However, in the walls of these sacs are types of cells. This gland consists of cells called follicular cells, which produces the hormones thyroxine and triiodothyronine. Also, there are parafollicular cells that make calcitonin.

1. *Thyroxine and Triiodothyronine* are known as T_3 and T_4. This is because thyroxine has 3 atoms of iodine and triiodothyronine has 4 atoms of iodine. These hormones regulate the action of the nervous system, growth of the body and metabolism.

2. *Calcitonin* is made when there is high amount of calcium in the blood. In this way, the calcium will go into the bones of the body.

Parathyroid Glands are located on the back of the thyroid glands. There is one inferior and superior parathyroid gland both on the right and left lateral thyroid lobes. This makes the parathyroid hormone.

1. *Parathyroid Hormone* takes calcium from bones and puts it into the blood when blood calcium levels are low. Paraythyroid hormone is made when there is a low amount of calcium in the blood. In this way, calcium will be taken out of the bone.

Adrenal Glands are located on top of each kidney. They are endocrine glands. The outer part of this gland is called the adrenal cortex and the inner part is referred to as the adrenal medulla. The adrenal glands produce the hormones aldosterone, epinephrine and cortisol.

1. *Aldosterone* is a hormone that increases blood levels of sodium and water. Low salt levels in the blood can produce low blood pressure and shock.

2. *Epinephrine (also known as Adrenaline)* is a hormone that gives the person fight or flight response. It does what the sympathetic nervous system does (explained on P.38).

3. *Cortisol* is a hormone that combats stressful situations in life. Trauma that can cause fear, infection, blood loss and starvation will lead to cortisol production.

Pancreas which is considered both an exocrine and endocrine gland is found in the abdomen area. It consists of a head, tail and body. The endocrine portion of the pancreas consists of tissue called the islets of Langerhans. The islets of Langerhans are composed of four types of cells: alpha cells, beta cells, delta cells and F-cells. These cells secrete or make hormones which include the following:

1. *Glucagon* is produced by the alpha cells. Glucagon raises blood sugar levels when it is below normal levels.

2. *Insulin* is produced by beta cells. Insulin decreases blood sugar levels (glucose) by putting the glucose into muscle to be used as fuel.

3. *Growth inhibiting hormone* is produced by the delta cells. It stops or inhibits the release of glucagon and insulin in the body.

4. *Pancreatic Polypeptide* is produced by the F-cells. They stop the release of pancreative digestive enzymes located in the exocrine portion of the pancreas.

Testes are endocrine glands, which are the testicles. The testes produce testosterone, which are important in the development of male sexual characteristics like facial hair and a deep voice. It also regulates the making of sperm.

Ovaries are endocrine glands that are located in both sides of the pelvis of a female. Ovaries synthesize female hormones called estrogen and progesterone. These hormones have a role in development of female sexual characteristics, menstrual cycle, lactation, and pregnancy.

Pineal Gland is an endocrine gland located in the brain. It produces the hormone melatonin. In fact, this hormone is produced during darkness. This is one reason why most people go to sleep at night. It may be suspected that increased levels of melatonin will make one more tired. It also may be the reason why people tend to be more tired in the winter months. Since there is less daylight in the winter, more melatonin is produced in humans.

Thymus gland is an endocrine gland that has an outer part called the cortex and inner part called the medulla. This gland is located above the heart. The thymus gland have hormones called thymopoietin and thymic factor that help in the maturation of T cells. T cells are types of lymphocytes (white blood cells) that fight against disease.

Diseases, Medical Terminology and Clinical Procedures

Cretinism is caused by low amounts of thyroid hormones being produced. Symptoms show the following: failure of the skeleton to fully mature, retardation and yellowish skin. This person will be very short.

Goiter (pronounced goy-ter) is an enlarged thyroid gland. This would show as an extreme swelling around the neck area looking tumor-like. This is caused by not getting enough iodine in the diet. If there is not enough iodine in the diet, their will be low levels of thyroid hormones in the body.

Human Growth Hormone Overproduction in children will cause gigantism (extreme tallness). In adults, it will cause acromegaly. Acromegaly will cause bones of the hands and feet to get larger. It will also cause facial features like the nose and jaw to get wider and bigger. Other bones of the face will also get bigger.

Hyperglycemia is high sugar (glucose) in the blood. If a person has this condition for a period of years, eventually diabetes mellitus (type II diabetes) will result. Diabetes mellitus is caused by overproduction of insulin. Insulin is produced and secreted to lower blood sugar levels. However, if a person constantly eats lots of foods filled with sugar (processed cakes, soda, and processed white bread) eventually the beta cells of the pancreas will wear out and stop producing enough insulin. In this way, there will be too much glucose in the blood.

Type II Diabetes occurs in people over 40 most commonly. Symptoms include the following: excess urine production, excessive appetite, and

excessive thirst. Because Type II diabetic patients have too much glucose in their blood, the glucose will eventually damage blood vessels in the body. This can lead to blindness if the arteries inside the eye are affected. If it affects the vessels of the heart, this can lead to heart attack. If it affects the vessels of the brain, it can cause a stroke. In addition, high glucose levels in the blood will cause nerve damage. This nerve damage can lead to not feeling pain as much. For example, this can lead to more injury.

Polyuria- refers to urinating large volumes frequently. This occurs with type II diabetes.

Polydipsia- refers to excessive thirst. This occurs with type II diabetes.

Polyphagia- refers to excessive hunger. This occurs with type II diabetes.

Exophthalmos (pronounced ek-sof-thal-mos) is a condition of bulging eyes from overproduction of thyroid hormones.

Thyroidectomy is the surgical removal of the thyroid gland.

XI. The Reproductive System

Structure and Function (Female/Male)

Male structures of the reproductive system include the following.

Scrotum is considered the skin around the testes. This skin supports the testes. In this skin is the dartos muscle. This muscle can wrinkle the skin of the scrotum.

Testes are referred to as the testicles. The testes rise by contraction of the cremaster muscle, which is an attachment of the internal oblique muscle. When the outside environment is too cold for the testicles, this muscle makes the testicles rise and get closer to the body. This is because the sperm in the testicles need a certain temperature to survive. However, the testes move away from the body when the temperature is too hot inside the testes. The testes must maintain a temperature a few degrees cooler than the body to protect the destruction of sperm. The structures are surrounded by a membrane called the tunica vaginalis and below that it is surrounded by the tunica albuginea. The layers around the testes first consists of the scrotum, then the tunica vaginalis and finally the tuncia albuginea.   In the tunica albuginea are compartments called lobules. In each lobule or compartment are seminiferous tubules where sperm are produced. The male hormone, testosterone is made by the interstitial cells of Leydig. These interstitial

cells are found the seminiferous tubules.

Epididymis is an organ found in the back or posterior part of each testis (testicle). It's about 1.5 to 1.7 inches long. It consists of a head, body and tail. In the epididymis are small continuous tubes called the ductus epididymis. This is the site where sperm mature to become fully fertile. They usually stay in this place for about 2 weeks after they are made. Sperm are first made in the seminiferous tubules. The sperm than goes to the epididymus, which consists of the ductus epididymus. The ductus epididymus is where sperm become mature and fertile. From the ductus epididymus the mature sperm enter a larger tube called the ductus deferens (vas deferens). Think of the testicles or testes as being filled with small and large tubes that are connected in order to produce and mature sperm.

Ductus Deferens is also known as the vas deferens. This structure is 18 inches in length. It is a tube connected to the ductus epididymus. The ductus deferens stores sperm. During an ejaculation, this stored sperm will go to the urethra of the penis and out of the body.

Spermatic Cord surrounds the ductus deferens. Around the ductus deferens are veins, arteries, nerves and the cremaster muscle. All of these structures are part of the spermatic cord.

Ampulla is the end portion of the ductus deferens. This is the portion closest to the urethra.

Urethra is the last duct that semen or urine enters until it goes out of the body by way of the external urethral orifice (opening). There are three parts of the urethra which are the following:
1. *Prostatic urethra* is the part that passes through the prostate gland.
2. *Membranous urethra*
3. *Spongy urethra* is the portion that is inside the penis.

Penis consists of certain portions. Each portion is made of tissue. The urethra inside the penis is surrounded directly by the corpus spongiosum. Surrounding the corpus spongiosum is the corpora cavernosa, which are both found in the body of the penis. The tip of the penis is a region called the glans penis.

Accessory Sex Glands secrete most of the liquid portion of semen. The accessory sex glands consists of the following:

1. Seminal Vesicles located near the ductus deferens. These structures put liquid around the sperm and thus creating 60% of the volume of semen. Semen contains fructose (sugar) that gives the sperm energy for movement once inside the vagina. Also, semen is considered a base (alkaline), which means it has a pH of above 7. This is to counteract or neutralize the acidic environment inside the vagina. If semen were not alkaline, all the sperm would die.

2. Prostate Gland is located below the urinary bladder. Its milky secretions makes up 25% of semen.

3. Cowper's Glands they are located below the prostate gland. They contribute to the liquid in semen.

Sperm Cell consists of a head, midpiece and a tail called the flagellum that propels or thrusts the sperm. The nucleus of the sperm cell, which is located in the head, contains the DNA (genetic information).

Structures of the female reproductive system are the following.

Ovaries are where the eggs are stored in the female. Each month an egg is set free each month during ovulation, which travels down the fallopian tube where the egg waits to get fertilized. The fallopian tube is part of the uterus. To fertilize the egg, sperm cells go from the vagina to the cervix (beginning structure of the uterus), to the main part of the uterus and then finally to the fallopian tube of the uterus to meet the egg. The ovarian ligament attaches the ovaries to the uterus. The suspensory ligament attaches the ovaries and uterus to the pelvic wall.

Uterus is the site where the embryo develops, menstruation occurs and the place for sperm to enter in order to get to the eggs. The broadest part of the uterus is called the fundus. The ampulla is the longest portion of the fallopian tube (uterine tube). Fertilization usually takes place in the ampulla. The inner epithelial layer of the uterus is called the endometrium. Part of this is shed each month during menstruation. The middle layer of the uterus is called the myometrium and the outer layer is called the perimetrium. The myometrium contains smooth muscles that contract during labor. Normally, the fetus should develop in the uterus.

Cervix is the narrow portion of the uterus that connects and opens into the vagina. The opening of the cervix to the vagina is called the external os.

Vagina is about 4 inches in length. It is made of inner transverse folds of connective tissue called rugae and a type of epithelium called stratified squamous. The vaginal orifice serves as the opening into the vagina.

Vulva refer to the external genitals of the female. The portion above the clitoris is called the *mons pubis*. The *mons pubis* contains fat and serves as a cushion during intercourse. The *labia majora* are the outer foldings of skin around the vagina. It also contains fat tissue The *labia minora* are the inner lips on both sides around the opening of the vagina. The *clitoris* is an erectile organ that contains many nerves. It gets enlarged with sexual excitement. The urethral orifice is located above the vaginal orifice. Urine comes out of the urethral orifice. There are glands around the vaginal orifice that secrete mucus for lubrication during sexual intercourse.

Mammary Glands are glands in the breasts that produce milk. The glands in the breasts secrete milk that passes out through the *lactiferous duct* and out through the nipple. The pigmented area around the nipple is called the *areola*. The size of the breast does not dictate how much milk can be secreted. The size of the breasts result from fat tissue not from the size of the mammary glands.

Menstruation occurs in the first 5 days of the menstrual cycle. Menstrual flow consists of endometrium tissue, blood and tissue fluid. The female reproductive cycle usually is between 28-33 days each month.

Phases of the Reproductive Cycle consists of three phases. The first phase is the menstrual cycle, which represents day 1 to day 5 of the reproductive cycle. The second phase consist of the preovulatory phase. This occurs between the menstruation and the actual time of ovulation. Ovulation or release of the egg from the ovary into the pelvic cavity occurs at day 15 of a 30 day female cycle. The postovulatory phase occurs between ovulation and the onset of menstruation.

Vasectomy is the surgical removal of a part of the ductus deferens. The actual procedure involves tying part of the ductus deferens so that to prevent sperm from entering the ejaculation. This procedure can be reversed in most cases.

Testicular Torsion (also known as a twisted testicle) is a condition where there is a twisting of the testicle on the spermatic cord. This twisting results in the blood vessels shutting off the blood supply to the testicle. This is considered a medical emergency. The spermatic cord must be untwisted within 12-24 hours after the occurrence or the patient could lose a testicle. This is because the testicle will die because of a lack of blood supply. The blood vessels are twisted cutting off blood supply. Signs of this condition include the following: extreme, unbearable, unrelenting, pounding pain around the testicular area, nausea, and vomiting. This usually occurs between the ages of 15 and 25. Speculations of causes may be from abnormal growth of spermatic cord, stress and certain types of heavy physical activity. However, the exact cause is not known.

Testicular Cancer occurs most commonly in males below the age of 40. Signs and symptoms are the following: large, hard, lump in the scrotum, enlarged testicle, and pain. Males who have testicles that don't descend into the scrotum by age 3 have a greater chance of getting testicular cancer.

Amenorrhea (pronounced a-men-o-re-a) refers to absence of menstruation. This is a condition of missing one or more periods. This can be caused by extreme physical activity. For example, female marathon runners sometimes experience amenorrhea. In addition, very thin females with anorexia may have amenorrhea. Amenorrhea can also be caused by a pituitary gland disorder.

Dysmenorrhea refers to having a painful menstruation.

Cryptorchidism is the condition of undescended testicles.

Prostatitis is an inflammation of the prostate gland that can be caused by a bacterial, viral or fungal infection. Symptoms and signs include the following: pain in the groin, chills and fever. Most bacterial causes of prostatitis occur from urinary tract infections by E. coli.

Colpotomy (pronounced kol-pot-o-me) is a surgical incision of the vagina.

Ectopic Pregnancy occurs when the fetus develops outside the uterus. Most commonly ectopic pregnancies occur in the fallopian tubes. However, they have been known to take place in the abdominal cavity and the cervix.

XII. Genetics

Chromosomes (Structure, Function, Types)

Genetics is the branch of biology that is associated with inheritance.

Chromosomes contain genetic material that is used to pass on certain traits to future generations. Each human cell in the body contains 46 chromosomes (23 pairs of chromosomes). Each chromosome has genes. There are over 100,000 genes in a cell. One chromosome in each pair comes from the father and one chromosome in each pair comes from the mother. This pair of chromosomes (two chromosomes) is called *homologues or homologous chromosomes.* Each pair of chromosomes contain genes that are specific for the same trait. For example, the two chromosomes in a pair contain the same gene for hair color at the same place of each homologous chromosome. They are referred to as *alleles* (pronounced ah-lelz). Abnormal alleles are referred to by a small letter as in the letter *a.* Normal alleles are referred to by a letter large as in the letter *A.* Possible allele combinations are the following: *AA, Aa or aa,* which are called **genotypes** *or genetic makeup.* People may have certain disorders or diseases if the genotype is *aa.* These small letters *aa* represent two abnormal alleles. *Aa* will not express a disease since the large *A* is a normal allele and the normal allele will be dominant over an abnormal allele (represented as small *a).* *AA* represents two normal alleles. In this way, *AA* will not express a disease. The following is to sum up allele letters:
1. *A* means the allele is a dominant trait.
2. *a* means the allele is a recessive trait.

There are times when dominant alleles will express a disease. For example, *AA* could express a disease also. There are times when *aa* could mean that a person will have fine body hair and not coarse body hair. In other words, recessive traits are not always bad.

Sex Chromosomes consists of an X and Y chromosome. The 23rd pair of chromosomes is considered the sex chromosomes. If a person has two X chromosomes, that person is female. If a person has one X and one Y chromosome, that person is male. The other 22 pairs of chromosomes that are not sex chromosomes are called *autosomes.*

Phenotype is the genetic makeup expressed physically in the body. For example, *Aa and AA* have the same genotypes but different phenotypes. However, *AA and aa* have different genotypes and phenotypes. People with the *Aa* allele are considered **carriers** of a gene. This is because the one small *a* in *Aa* can be expressed as two *aa* in the carrier's children.

Genome is the entire genetic makeup of a person. Each trait of a person is encoded by a gene.

Genes, DNA, RNA, Inheritance of Sex and Somatic Traits

Gene has the code necessary to make one protein. Genes are located in precise positions on a chromosome.

Locus is the precise position of a gene on a chromosome.

DNA is referred to as deoxyribonucleic acid. This is basically the cell's genetic material. DNA is a double helix structure. It is similar to a spiral staircase in structure. DNA is composed of sugar called deoxyribose, phosphate molecules, and bases (thymine, adenine, cytosine and guanine). The bases are made of nitrogen. Bases form the genetic code in each cell of the body. The bases are the steps of the staircase and the phosphate molecules are the outer connected edges of each step. The following bases always pair together:
1. *adenine -- thymine*
2. *cytosine -- guanine.*

RNA is referred to as ribonucleic acid. RNA spreads specific directions from the DNA to direct each cell's making of amino acids into proteins. RNA forms on one side of the DNA when needed proteins needed to be made. RNA contains the following bases and are paired in the following way:
1. *adenine -- uracil*
2. *cytosine-- guanine*
As you can see, uracil is substituted as a base instead of thymine. When RNA is completely formed, it separates from the DNA. RNA is now a complete copy of the genetic information of the DNA. This RNA copy is called *messenger RNA (mRNA)*. This messenger RNA goes to the

ribosomes (structure of the cell that makes proteins). The messenger RNA tells the ribosomes what kind of protein should be made. It's kind of like a waiter telling the chef what type of food the customer wants. Amino acids are brought also by a type of RNA called *transfer RNA (tRNA)*. Now the amino acids are made in the ribosome to make protein (made up lots of amino acids).

Inheritance of Sex is determined by the 23rd pair of chromosomes. These two chromosomes normally can be XX or XY. XX means the person will be female. XY means the person will be male.

Inheritance of Somatic Traits (traits in the body) is not based only on dominant-recessive inheritance as explained before. In fact, most inheritance is based on more than one gene interacting. Also, one gene can affect more than one physical trait. For now, here are some examples of dominant and recessive traits.

Recessive	Dominant
Flat Feet	Normal arches
Thin lips	Large lips
No Freckles	Freckles
20/20 vision	Nearsightedness (can't see far)
Little eyes	Big eyes
Unable to hear (deafness)	Able to hear

Genes/Environment Interaction (Genotype vs Phenotype)

The phenotypic expression (physical expression) of a gene is influenced by other genotypes (genetic makeup) and the environment. In other words, the environment has a major influence if a gene will be physically expressed. For example, if a child has genes that says he should be 6 feet tall (*his genotype*), extreme malnutrition may lead to the person being a couple of inches shorter. Another example, a person might have genes that say she should be very physically strong (*her genotype*). However, without enough dietary protein, her muscles cannot reach their full potential of strength.

Codominant Inheritance refers to inheriting both genes and expressing the phenotypes of both genes. In other words, both genes are expressed. A

person having alleles for Type A blood and alleles for Type B blood will have Type AB blood. This person has traits of both Type A blood and Type B blood.

Polygenic Inheritance refers that many inherited traits are controlled by more than one gene. A physical trait will then result from the influence of many genes. These many genes are called polygenes. A polygenic trait is one's hair color.

Genetic Basis for Disorders

Klinefelter's Syndrome is caused by having one extra X chromosome. This person would have the configuration of XXY, which means the person would be male. However, a normal male has the genetic code XY. Having an extra X would lead to the following signs: small testes, infertility, breast development, small amount of body hair. This syndrome occurs in 1 out of 700 births.

Down's Syndrome is also referred to as trisomy 21. This is caused by an extra chromosome to appear on the paired chromosome 21. Normally, a person should have only 46 chromosomes. However, with Down's syndrome the person has 47 chromosomes. Signs of this condition include the following: low set ears, lack of a fold in the palms, slanting eyes, mental retardation, short in height, flat face, short fingers and hearing problems. Life expectancy is usually in the 40's. However, some can live past 80 years of age. This syndrome occurs in 1 in 700 births. If the mother is 35, it occurs in 1 in 350 births. If a mother is over 45, the risk of Down's syndrome is 1 in 25 births.

Edwards' Syndrome is also referred to as trisomy 18. This is caused by an extra chromosome to appear on the paired chromosome 18. Signs of this condition include the following: clubfeet, heart defects, webbed hands, small head, facial defects and mental retardation. Patients with this condition only live a few months. This occurs in 1 in 3500 births.

Turner's Syndrome occurs in females. This occurs when one of the two sex chromosomes is absent. A normal female should have two XX sex chromosomes. A female with this disorder has only one X sex chromosome. Signs include he following: short, webbed neck, low hairline, dropping eyelids, short nails, no periods (amenorrhea), sterility and usually there is not mental retardation.

Triple X Syndrome occurs when a person has three X sex chromosomes. The configuration would be XXX. This person is female and occurs in 1 in 950 births. Signs include the following: sterility can develop and lower intelligence levels.

Patau's Syndrome is also known as trisomy 13. There is an extra chromosome on the 13th chromosome. Signs include the following: there is a space between the upper lips (cleft lip), deformity in ears, heart defects and mental retardation.

Titles Available from Silver Educational Publishing

Spinal Anatomy Study Guide: Key Review Questions and Answers

Histology Study Guide: Key Review Questions and Answers

Anatomy and Physiology Study Guide: Key Review Questions and Answers with Explanations (Volume 1)

Anatomy and Physiology Study Guide: Key Review Questions and Answers with Explanations (Volume 2)

Microbiology Study Guide: Key Review Questions and Answers

National Board of Chiropractic Part I Study Guide: Key Review Questions and Answers

National Board of Chiropractic Part II Study Guide: Key Review Questions and Answers

National Board of Chiropractic Part III Study Guide: Key Review Questions and Answers with Explanations

The Ultimate Study Guide for the National Certification Examination for Therapeutic Massage and Bodywork: Key Review Questions and Answers
Topics: Human Anatomy, Physiology and Kinesiology (Volume 1)

The Ultimate Study Guide for the National Certification Examination for Therapeutic Massage and Bodywork: Key Review Questions and Answers
Topics: Clinical Pathology & Recognition of Various Conditions (Volume 2)

The Ultimate Study Guide for the National Certification Examination for Therapeutic Massage and Bodywork: Key Review Questions and Answers
Topics: Massage Therapy and Bodywork: Theory, Assessment and Application. Professional Standards, Ethics & Business Practices (Volume 3)

Go to our website at www.SEPBOOKS.com to order direct. These titles are also available at www.amazon.com or your college bookstore.